TOWARDS A SMOKE-FREE GENERATION

Campaign manual

Health
Education
Authority

2

Acknowledgments

This manual was written on behalf of the
Health Education Authority and
Department of Health by Bill Bellew and
Iain Ramsay. The authors are grateful to all
those who gave of their time and advice. In
particular, thanks to Sandra Bourne, Jerry
Bird, Anne Charlton, Lesley De Meza, Joyce
Epstein, Lynda Finn, Martin Jarvis, Ruth
Joyce, Andrew McCulloch, Donald Reid,
David Rivett, Keith Tones, Chloe West and
Kate Woodhouse.

Published in 1991 by the
Health Education Authority

© Health Education Authority 1991

Health Education Authority
Hamilton House
Mabledon Place
London WC1H 9TX

ISBN 1 85448 270 X

Printed in Great Britain by Scotprint Ltd, Musselburgh

Contents

3

Foreword   7

About the Manual   9

**Towards a Smoke-free Generation: Action
Summary**   11

Introduction   13
   Aim   13
   Programme strategies   15
   Some facts about smoking at a glance   15

SECTION 1. **Impact of Smoking on Health**   17

Why tobacco smoke is a danger to health   17
   Nicotine   17
   Tar   18
   Carbon monoxide   18
The short-term effects of smoking   18
The long-term effects of smoking   18
   Coronary heart disease (CHD)   18
   Chronic obstructive lung disease (COLD)   19
   Lung cancer   19
The risks to non-smokers   19

SECTION 2. **Young People and Smoking**   21

Prevalence   21
Immediate health risks   22
The first cigarette   23
Nicotine dependence in young people   23
Smoking and weight control   23
Becoming a smoker   24
   Developing the habit   24

SECTION 3. **Influences on Smoking and Non-smoking**   25

Why do young people smoke?   25
Personal factors   26
   What can we do?   28
The influence of the family   29
   What can we do?   29
Friends and groups identified with   30

CONTENTS

4

What can we do?	30
Factors relating to school	31
What can we do?	31
Factors relating to the community	31
What can we do?	32
Factors relating to the wider environment	32
What can we do?	32
To smoke or not to smoke?	32
1. Is the threat to health serious?	32
2. Is the threat personal to me?	33
3. What will I lose by deciding to give up smoking?	33
4. What will I gain by deciding to stop smoking?	33

SECTION 4. Smoking and the Curriculum 35

The personal, social and health education context	35
The National Curriculum	36
Guidance from the National Curriculum Council	36
Age, stage and development	37
Primary school	37
Secondary school	38
Ability	38
Co-ordination	38
Curriculum audit	39
Content, delivery and timing	39
Content	40
Delivery	40
Timing	40
The teacher's role	46
What can teachers do?	47
What can schools do?	47
Implications for action	47

SECTION 5. Towards an Effective School Smoking Policy: An Overview 49

Smoking by teachers	49
Smoking by pupils	50
No smoking v designated smoking areas	50
Teachers' attitudes to smoking at school	50
Towards an effective policy	50
Rationale	50
Implementing a smoke-free school policy: a checklist	52
Effective disciplinary procedures	52

SECTION 6.	School-based Prevalence Surveys	53

Why school surveys are needed		53
How you can use the results		53
When and how to conduct surveys		53
Smoking questionnaire		55

5

SECTION 7.	Appendices	57

Appendix i	Objectives of the National Programme	57
Appendix ii	Advertising	58
Appendix iii	Tobacco Consumption	62
Appendix iv	Parents Against Tobacco	64
Appendix v	SmokeBusters	66
Appendix vi	Useful Addresses	67
Appendix vii	References	69
Appendix viii	Orientation: School Checklist	74

Towards a smoke-free generation evaluation sheet		75

The national programme features mass media and publicity campaigns.

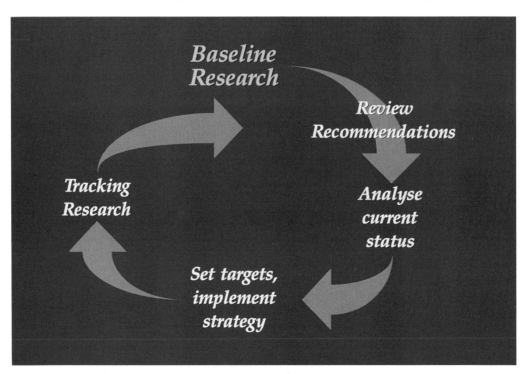

Baseline research was conducted immediately before the launch; bi-annual tracking research informs strategic planning.

Foreword

In December 1989 the largest ever integrated attempt to tackle the epidemic of smoking among young people in England was launched. The aim is significantly to reduce smoking among young people. The programme, co-ordinated by the Health Education Authority with the Department of Health and the Department of Education and Science, is being run in collaboration with district health authorities, local authorities, ASH, TACADE and major health charities.

Smoking remains by far the major preventable cause of disease and early death in the UK and, while a variety of strategies over the years have contributed to a reduction in the number of adults smoking, new generations of smokers continue to be recruited to smoking in their teens or at an even earlier age. At present the majority of smokers take up the habit before the age of 16. Concern about the number of young people who continue to take up smoking has led to this national programme.

Research has shown that school health education can play a major part in reducing the number of teenagers smoking. It is intended therefore that the national programme will build on existing activities in schools and colleges. However, given the addictive nature of smoking, its associations with adulthood and the sophisticated way in which tobacco products are advertised and marketed, a variety of additional strategies are required to support school-based activities if we are to be successful in reducing the number of young people smoking.

Curriculum projects and other activities for youth settings are key elements, as are the major publicity and mass media campaigns which are also featured, and the research which is being conducted to track the success

8

of the programme.

For teachers and schools with a long tradition of working in smoking and health education, the national programme provides a new framework within which to continue and develop their work. In schools where this tradition is less established the programme provides the opportunity to become more involved through curricular projects, school policy development, home-school links and wider community action. It is important that young people have the opportunity to develop the skills and understanding required to resist pressures to smoke. It is easier for them to do so in a supportive environment where non-smoking is regarded as the norm, and the right to breathe smoke-free air is respected.

This programme seeks to enlist the support of local authorities, district and regional health authorities, schools and colleges, on whom its success will ultimately depend. By becoming involved you will make an important contribution to the health and well-being of future generations, by helping to eliminate misery caused by smoking-related diseases. Your involvement can help our society to take another important step towards a smoke-free generation.

About the Manual

This manual is designed for use by all those involved in the education of young people in primary, middle and secondary schools. It provides a guide to effective strategies in health education about smoking and contains background information on the issues that teachers may encounter.

- Read this section and the Action Summary first.
- Go directly to the section you need.
- Don't expect to use all of the manual!
- Appendices and detailed references are included for more in-depth study.

Introduction   Introduces the new national programme to reduce the prevalence of smoking among teenagers, its rationale and objectives.

Section 1.   **Impact of Smoking on Health**
Provides an update on the health risks from smoking and from breathing other people's tobacco smoke, illustrating the cause for concern and the need for action.

Section 2.   **Young People and Smoking**
Examines recent research about the prevalence of smoking among young people and looks at the short-term effects and immediate health risks faced by young people who smoke.

Section 3.   **Influences on Smoking and Non-smoking**
Identifies the factors influencing teenage smoking, summarises recent research findings and points to implications for health educators.

Section 4.   **Smoking and the Curriculum**
Suggests approaches within the framework of personal, social and health education and the National Curriculum. Examines content, timing, delivery and the role of the teacher.

Section 5.   **Towards an Effective School Smoking Policy: an Overview**
Provides an overview of the issues surrounding smoking by

10

pupils, staff and others who work in schools or use school premises. Summarises recent research into what makes an effective school smoking policy.

Section 6.   **School-based Prevalence Surveys**
Explains how to conduct a school-based survey of smoking. Provides a model survey form.

Section 7.   **Appendices**

Appendix i	Objectives of the National Programme
Appendix ii	Advertising
Appendix iii	Tobacco Consumption
Appendix iv	Parents Against Tobacco
Appendix v	SmokeBusters
Appendix vi	Useful Addresses
Appendix vii	References
Appendix viii	Orientation: School Checklist

Towards a Smoke-free Generation: Action Summary

The individual

- Ideally, implement a systematic programme for ages 9–16 in the form of a spiral curriculum with special attention to the time of transfer and gender.

The family

- Involve parents and governors in the development of a smoking programme through the PTA and other means available.

- Introduce parents to the new national programme to reduce teenage smoking.

- Introduce smoking bans and rationale at parents' evenings.

- Raise the following issues with parents:

  - the hazards of smoking and passive smoking
  - the risks to young people
  - the important role of parents in smoking education
  - how parental attitudes can influence young people's smoking
  - helping to reduce the illegal sale of cigarettes
  - monitoring breaches in advertising codes for tobacco products as they relate to young people
  - lobbying for smoke-free public transport and public places
  - district health authority initiatives related to smoking.

Friends and groups

- Curricular programme has specific relevance, e.g. understanding peer

12

pressure, referral skills, coping mechanisms.

- Be aware of the social reference groups outside school and the activities that young people are involved in.

- Liaise with other agencies running clubs, discos, sports events, and provide smoke-free opportunities.

- Make information available about 'SmokeBusters' clubs.

- Lobby for smoke-free leisure centres, shopping arcades, swimming pools, discos, fast food outlets, etc.

School

- Work towards a written formal policy covering pupils, staff and all who use or work in the building, etc.

- Implement the policy consistently and with commitment from staff.

- Prevent pupils from smoking and restrict smoking by adults.

- Devise appropriate strategies; time curricular components accurately.

  - Adopt an extensive cross-curricular approach spanning primary and secondary schools since children as young as 9 are known to try smoking and experimentation with smoking peaks at ages 11–14.

  - Educate *before* as well as during the years when young people begin to experiment with smoking. This has been shown to have a positive effect on knowledge and behaviour.

  - Use surveys and class activities to identify attitudes to smoking, smoking behaviour and smoking prevalence.

  - Make young people aware of the *immediate* dangers of smoking.

  - Reduce opportunities to smoke at school and elsewhere.

- Create an environment where non-smoking is the norm and young people are not exposed to adults smoking.

Community

- Find out about and undertake the activity promoted through the Parents Against Tobacco (PAT) campaign.

- Liaise with the district health authority.

- Liaise with other community groups trying to promote non-smoking as the norm.

- Help to monitor advertising and notify COMATAS (see Appendix vi) of any breaches of the advertising code.

- Help to monitor the availability of cigarettes and their illegal sale to children.

- Develop links with youth networks, mass media and other organisations to discuss, debate and press for positive action in relation to advertising, illegal sales and provision of smoke-free places.

Wider environment

- Motivate and influence people to campaign for positive action on:

  - sales promotion
  - advertising (see Appendix ii)
  - taxation (see Appendix iii)
  - greater provision of smoke-free environments (see Appendix v).

Introduction

Aim

Programme strategies

Some facts about smoking at a glance

Aim

The overall aim of the teenage smoking programme is to reduce smoking among 11–15-year-olds in England by one-third before November 1994. Initially, the focus will be on the 11–13 age group.[1] Special attention will be devoted to the year following transfer to secondary school: research[2] has shown that this is a key time when young people may experiment with cigarettes and take up smoking.

Age of transfer may vary from one local authority to another but it seems that it is the process of transfer[3] which is important and not the actual age when it takes place.

Attention will focus on other age groups later in the programme. (See Figure 1.) The programme objectives are listed in Appendix i (page 57).

Teach her a lesson. Cut out the coupon.

Initially the focus will be on the 11–13 age group.

14

TARGET GROUPS

Associated target group			Main target group					Associated target group			
age	9	10	* 11	12	13	14	15	16	17	18	19
			Target group for reduction in smoking by 1994								

* Transfer (the exact age of transfer may vary among LEAs)

[shaded box] Core target group

New National Curriculum description

AGE	DESCRIPTION	ABBREVIATION
5 or under	Reception	R
5–7	Years 1 and 2	Y1–2
7–11	Years 3 to 6	Y3–6
11–14	Years 7 to 9	Y7–9
14–16	Years 10 and 11	Y10–11

Figure 1. *Target groups for the national programme*

Broadly speaking, pupils in key stage 1 will be in Reception, Year 1 or Year 2; those in key stage 2 in Years 3 to 6; those in key stage 3 in Years 7 to 9; and those in key stage 4 in Years 10 and 11.

Programme strategies

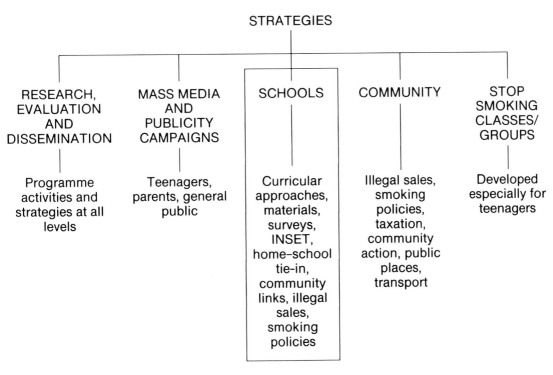

Figure 2. *Strategies to reduce teenage smoking*

The national programme features mass media and publicity campaigns aimed at influencing young people's attitudes to smoking, and seeking the support of parents and the general public in the campaign. The success of a programme such as this depends very much on schools, parents, health professionals and youth organisations to provide the interpersonal element which is essential to complement the mass media work.[4]

An expert panel[1] has suggested that it is inadvisable overtly to link a mass media component with school health education. Teenagers, particularly older ones, may reject messages with a stamp of authority on them. A direct connection between school lessons and the media campaign could undermine the effectiveness of the latter with the target audience. However, if pupils themselves raise issues because of their awareness of mass media, this should not deter teachers from using such an opportunity to enhance learning.

Some facts about smoking at a glance

- In the 12 months to June 1988 the tobacco industry spent £113.5 million on advertising.[5]

- In 1989, around 95.5 billion cigarettes were released for home consumption in the UK and consumers spent £8.2 billion on cigarettes and other tobacco products.

- It is estimated that 110,000 people die prematurely each year from smoking and other smoking attributable diseases in Great Britain.[6]

- The cost of treatment of smoking attributable diseases in the National Health Service in 1987–88 was estimated at about £500 million;[7] the overall cost of cigarette smoking to the nation has been estimated at £4,000 million.[8]

- For the first time in recent years cigarette consumption in the UK is on the increase; UK figures show that expenditure increased by 0.3 per cent between 1988 and 1989. Excluding inflation, this is an increase of £18 million.

- It is widely acknowledged that school children are sold some £70 million worth of cigarettes illegally each year.

- Young people who inhale smoke increase the risk of coughs and respiratory problems. Smoking causes changes in their bodies which can increase the risk of heart disease in later life and impair lung function.[9]

- Young people who smoke tend to be absent more from school, are more likely to be under-achievers, and to achieve lower grades overall than non-smokers.[10,11]

- From the age of 14 to 17 more girls than boys are regular smokers.[12]

- Among 15-year-olds, 17 per cent of boys and 24 per cent of girls smoke every week.[12]

Each year school children are sold some £70 million worth of cigarettes illegally.

Impact of Smoking on Health

Why tobacco smoke is a danger to health

The short-term effects of smoking

The long-term effects of smoking

The risks to non-smokers

Why tobacco smoke is a danger to health

Tobacco smoke contains over 4,000[13] different chemicals, 43[14] of which are complete carcinogens (cancer causing substances) in their own right. The following components of tobacco smoke have been identified as being most likely to cause disease.

Nicotine

When tobacco is burned, nicotine is transferred to the smoke, attaching itself to tiny droplets of tar. When the smoke is inhaled the tar is deposited on the lining of the respiratory tract and the lungs, and the nicotine is absorbed into the bloodstream. Nicotine is a powerful and addictive[15] drug which takes seven seconds to reach the brain.

It has a number of immediate effects on the body:[16]

- It acts on the central nervous system and the autonomic nervous system mimicking the action of natural neurotransmitters, the substances which conduct nerve impulses in these systems. In small doses, nicotine generally stimulates nerve impulses and in large doses it inhibits them.
- It increases the heart rate and blood pressure.
- It causes constriction of the small blood vessels under the skin.

In the long term, nicotine:

- may be a factor in causing coronary heart disease;
- can play a part in reproductive and gastrointestinal disorders.

18

Tar

When cigarette smoke is inhaled it condenses and about 70 per cent of the tar content is deposited in the lungs.[17] The cancer causing properties of tobacco are particularly related, but not confined, to the tar. When cooled, tar is a sticky brown substance which can stain smokers' fingers and teeth a yellow-brown colour. It also stains the lung tissue. Irritants in tar can cause damage to the lungs by causing narrowing of the bronchioles, coughing, increase in bronchial mucus and harm to the cilia.

Carbon monoxide

This is a poisonous gas which combines with haemoglobin, the substance which carries oxygen in the blood. It combines with the haemoglobin 200 times[18] more readily than oxygen, and therefore reduces the blood's ability to carry oxygen. Because oxygen is essential to all tissues, shortage of it can be dangerous, particularly for people with heart disease.[19] Angina and other conditions associated with reduced arterial blood supply are made worse by even small amounts of carbon monoxide. It is especially harmful during pregnancy as it reduces the amount of oxygen being carried to the developing baby.

Carbon monoxide can also affect the electrical activity of the heart, increase the permeability of arterial walls to cholesterol and, in conjunction with haemoglobin, is related to the thickening of artery walls, which can cause circulatory problems.[20]

The short-term effects of smoking

- The irritant substances in tobacco smoke can cause a build-up of phlegm and a smoker's cough.
- Smokers are more likely than non-smokers to get chest infections as smoking reduces the ability of the lungs to fight infections.

- Tobacco smoke reduces the efficiency of the lungs, making people more breathless than they would normally be during exercise or sudden physical exertion.
- New smokers learn to inhale cigarette smoke and can quickly become dependent on nicotine.
- Experienced smokers learn to maintain the amount of nicotine in their bloodstream and when nicotine levels go down they crave more strongly for tobacco.
- Maintaining nicotine levels helps to reduce withdrawal symptoms and therefore keeps people addicted to tobacco.

The long-term effects of smoking

Generally, the worst health effects of smoking do not appear for many years. Because of this, young people tend to dismiss the risk of smoking-related diseases. By contrast, their concern is about their immediate environment and the social and psychological usefulness of smoking tobacco. Smoking is highly addictive, however, and if young people continue with the habit they may later develop one of the three main categories of disease caused by smoking. These are:

Coronary heart disease (CHD)

CHD is now the leading cause of death in this and many other developed countries. In 1988,[21] 153,084 people in England and Wales died from this disease, 27,553 of them before the age of 65. The risk of dying from CHD is two and a half times greater for a smoker than for a non-smoker and three times greater for a heavier smoker.

There is evidence[22] that the beginnings of circulation problems related to heart disease are already visible in young people who smoke.

Chronic obstructive lung disease (COLD)

The most familiar COLDs are bronchitis and emphysema. Most people suffering from these conditions are smokers. In 1988, there were 28,749 deaths from chronic obstructive pulmonary disease (International Classification of Diseases (ICDs) 490–496) in England and Wales. Of these, 4,121 were people under the age of 65.[21] The younger people are when they become regular smokers and the more cigarettes they smoke, the greater the risk of COLD when they are older.[20]

Lung cancer

An estimated 90 per cent of lung cancers are caused by smoking. In 1988,[21] 35,302 people died of the disease (International Classification of Diseases 162) in England and Wales. Lung cancer is about to replace breast cancer as the most common cause of death from cancer among women.

The younger people become regular smokers and the more cigarettes they smoke, the greater the risk of lung cancer.[20] Other diseases and symptoms related to smoking include:[23]

Heart and circulatory diseases

Congestive cardiac and ventricular failure
Angina pectoris – increases in both incidence and severity
Atherosclerosis which leads to vascular disease and circulation problems, e.g. Buerger's disease which can result in leg amputation
Stroke

Lung diseases

Recurrent respiratory infections
Impairment of lung function

Cancers

Mouth
Pharynx and larynx
Oesophagus
Pancreas
Bladder
Cervix
Leukaemia

Other

Peptic ulcers – an increase in incidence and the time they take to heal
Tobacco amblyopia – a form of blindness

Smoking can also increase the incidence and severity of complaints which people tend not to perceive as being related to their smoking: coughs, wheezing and shortness of breath on exertion.

Women face additional risks. Smoking is a risk factor for cervical cancer. Women who smoke and take the contraceptive pill have an increased risk of having a stroke or heart attack. Smoking can cause complications during pregnancy and harm the developing baby. Mothers who smoke put their own health at risk but also expose their babies or young children to the risks of passive smoking.[24]

The best investment that anyone can make in their health is never to take up smoking. For those who do smoke, breaking free of the habit is probably the greatest single thing they can do to improve their health.

Figure 3 illustrates the seriousness of the threat to health from smoking; the additional risks faced by women who smoke; the importance of preventing young people from taking up the habit; and the need to help people to stop smoking.

The risks to non-smokers

Originally, research into the health hazards of smoking focused just on the smoker. In recent years, however, the effects on non-smokers of breathing other people's tobacco smoke have been examined. Breathing second-hand smoke is called *passive smoking*.

In 1988, the Independent Scientific Committee on Smoking and Health[25] concluded that several hundred lung cancer deaths each year could be attributed to passive smoking. People who have never smoked but have been exposed to tobacco smoke throughout most of their lives have a 10–30 per cent higher risk of lung cancer than non-smokers not exposed in this way.

Many people find that tobacco smoke causes:

Sore or runny eyes	Wheezing
Sneezing	Hoarseness
Runny nose	Stuffed-up feeling
Headaches	Coughing

People with asthma may find that breathing other people's tobacco smoke brings on an attack. People with allergies often find that tobacco smoke makes their condition worse.

Many contact lens wearers find that tobacco smoke affects their vision, and some may become more prone to eye infection.

For some children the consequences of breathing other people's tobacco smoke go beyond the nuisance level. The children of smokers are more likely to get middle ear infections, bronchitis, pneumonia and other chest infections than the children of non-smokers.[9]

Non-smoking children whose parents both smoke can inhale the nicotine equivalent of 100[26] cigarettes in a year. Children who suffer from asthma are particularly at risk from tobacco smoke in the home.

Figure 3. *The risks to health faced by men and women who smoke*

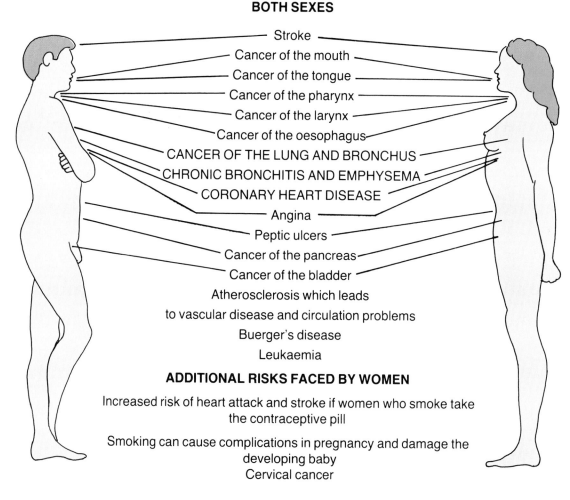

BOTH SEXES

Stroke

Cancer of the mouth

Cancer of the tongue

Cancer of the pharynx

Cancer of the larynx

Cancer of the oesophagus

CANCER OF THE LUNG AND BRONCHUS

CHRONIC BRONCHITIS AND EMPHYSEMA

CORONARY HEART DISEASE

Angina

Peptic ulcers

Cancer of the pancreas

Cancer of the bladder

Atherosclerosis which leads to vascular disease and circulation problems

Buerger's disease

Leukaemia

ADDITIONAL RISKS FACED BY WOMEN

Increased risk of heart attack and stroke if women who smoke take the contraceptive pill

Smoking can cause complications in pregnancy and damage the developing baby

Cervical cancer

Young People and Smoking

Prevalence

Immediate health risks

The first cigarette

Nicotine dependence in young people

Smoking and weight control

Becoming a smoker

Prevalence

Recent research on smoking among secondary school children in England[12] has revealed the following:

Boys and girls
- Smoking remains more prevalent among girls than boys (i.e. a higher percentage).
- Among those who do smoke, boys continue to smoke more cigarettes than girls (i.e. more heavily).
- Boys tend to experiment with smoking earlier than girls.
- Overall, girls are more likely to become regular smokers at ages 14 and 15.

Home influence
- Young people are more likely to be smokers if other people at home smoke, with siblings seeming to exert more influence than parents in this respect.
- When a parent smokes, children are more than twice as likely to be regular smokers than if neither parent smokes.

Illegal sales
- It is estimated that in an average week about a quarter of a million children are sold cigarettes illegally (under the age of 16).

Experimentation
Most experimentation with smoking occurs in late childhood and early adolescence. Studies confirm that it peaks between the ages of 11 and 14 and half of all children who experiment with smoking before they are 16 do so in the first three years of secondary school.[12]

The period between the ages of 9 and 10

has been identified as a time for experimenting with a first cigarette.[2] Curiosity and the fact that others are trying smoking play an important role in early experimentation. The cigarette is usually obtained from another person and smoked in the company of others.

Experimenting is frequently kept secret from parents and, for young secondary pupils, school is one of the places where they are likely to experiment.[27]

Regular smoking
- Few children are regular smokers at 11 but by the age of 15 about one in six boys (17 per cent) and one in four girls (24 per cent) smoke regularly (at least one cigarette a week).[12]

Table 1.

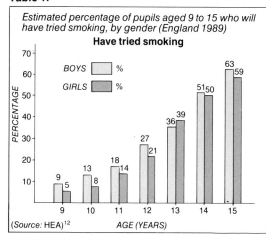

Estimated percentage of pupils aged 9 to 15 who will have tried smoking, by gender (England 1989)
(Source: HEA)[12]

Table 2.

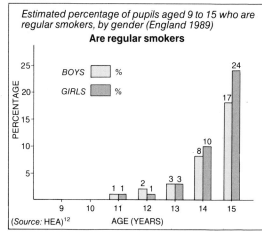

Estimated percentage of pupils aged 9 to 15 who are regular smokers, by gender (England 1989)
(Source: HEA)[12]

Consumption
- Boys tend to smoke more cigarettes than girls. In the week prior to the survey, 21 per cent of boys and 29 per cent of girls had smoked. On average, the boys smoked 32 and the girls 26 cigarettes.[12]

Immediate health risks

For youngsters the major smoking attributable diseases – lung cancer, chronic obstructive lung disease and coronary heart disease – are perceived as personally irrelevant. Most young people are mainly concerned about the present and tend not to think about what might happen to their health in the future. They often believe that they can smoke now and, if they choose, stop when they are adults. They tend to think that they are immortal. It is therefore important to make young people aware of the *immediate* short-term effects of smoking on their health. These include:

- increased heart rate
- rise in blood pressure
- reduction in skin temperature
- increased mucus resulting in coughing
- cilia damage, making smokers more prone to chest infections
- reduction in fitness because of increased levels of carbon monoxide in the lungs
- reduction in steadiness of the hand
- becoming addicted to nicotine, leading to difficulty in stopping smoking.

By showing pupils the immediate effects of smoking on their health, it becomes harder for them to dismiss the effects as not being relevant to them. Using a carbon monoxide monitor is one way of demonstrating the immediate effects.

Smoking among teenagers can cause sore throats, chest infections, coughs and shortness of breath.[28] Research has shown that teenagers who smoke look on these ailments as minor and acceptable and not related in any way to their smoking. Demonstrating the immediate effects of nicotine, carbon monoxide and tar on the body can prove effective in leading young people to an understanding of the damage they can do to their bodies by smoking.

It is essential that the guidance provided by the DES[29] and the Association of Science Education[30] is followed.

Any work of this nature should also be supported by the other educational approaches discussed in this manual (see Section 4).

Important as it is to focus on the short-term effects, people must not lose sight of the long-term risks. We know that the incidence of lung cancer depends on how long people have been smoking, and that the risk of dying from coronary heart disease is higher for those who start to smoke regularly early in their lives.[31] These findings underline the importance of preventing young people from starting to smoke, and helping those who have already started to stop smoking.

Exploring the long-term effects of smoking can be built into a programme at a later stage in the pupils' development. Teachers should note that scare tactics about smoking attributable diseases are not usually effective in lessons with young people.

The first cigarette

Vomiting, dizziness or diarrhoea after a first cigarette may be experienced by some young people, but not by all. Those who experience such symptoms may soon overcome these effects and develop a tolerance to tobacco smoke. After smoking regularly they may find that if they don't have a cigarette they begin to crave for one. They may also find that they become irritable and do not sleep well without the level of nicotine they have come to need.

Nicotine dependence in young people

Although young people begin to smoke for a variety of social and psychological reasons, they can quickly become dependent on the pharmacological effects of nicotine.[32] As they are often unaware of, or underestimate, the strength of tobacco addiction, it is important that they understand that smoking is an *addictive behaviour* which can be difficult to stop.

Dependence, real or imagined, can make it difficult for young people to stop. Any discussion about addiction must be handled with care so as not to justify the habit – 'What's the point? I'm addicted now.' They should be reminded of the challenge of giving up smoking, the benefits to them personally, and the fact that over 11 million people have managed to stop successfully in the UK alone.

Smoking and weight control

Many smokers worry about putting on weight if they stop smoking, and think of themselves as controlling their weight through their smoking. The concern about weight gain is about physical appearance rather than health in a wider context.[33] Research has shown that any resulting weight reduction from smoking is too small to counteract the benefits of stopping. Smoking is an extremely unhealthy way to control weight. Young people, particularly young women, need to be aware of this, and any work in this area clearly needs to be set in a context of lessons about body image, sexist stereotyping, nutrition and exercise. Young women also need to be aware that the tobacco industry plays on the desire for slimness in marketing techniques aimed at women.

Becoming a smoker

Young people rarely become regular smokers overnight. They usually drift into smoking through a predictable sequence which can take two years or longer to unfold.[34] The sequence can be represented as follows:

Figure 4. *Developing the habit*

STAGE	AGE
Non-smoker	5–6
Contemplating smoking	6–8
Preparing to experiment	
First experimentation	9–10
More extensive experimentation	11–13
Developing the habit	14 +
Regular smoker	15 +

Although there are peak times for experimentation, we have to be aware that, whether in primary or secondary school, individual pupils may be at different stages in this sequence.

At each stage there is an opportunity for opting out and an opportunity for promoting non-smoking can be seized. It is therefore important to know where young people are in their thinking about smoking, and what their current smoking behaviour is before embarking on a curricular programme. This can be ascertained by using school and class surveys (see Section 6).

Movement between experimentation, regular smoking and even stopping for short or longer periods is fairly fluid among teenagers. Experimentation in early adolescence does not point irrevocably to being a smoker later in life, but it is a strong predictor. If young people have not started smoking by their late teens, however, they are less likely to become smokers.

Developing the habit

The development of smoking is a gradual process and it can take a considerable time for smokers to acknowledge that they are regular smokers. Buying cigarettes is an early part of smoking behaviour. Inhaling and increasing consumption gradually follow, and eventually individuals begin to see themselves as smokers and start to smoke more openly in front of others.[34]

Influences on Smoking and Non-smoking

Why do young people smoke?

Personal factors

The influence of the family

Friends and groups identified with

Factors relating to school

Factors relating to the community

Factors relating to the wider environment

To smoke or not to smoke?

Why do young people smoke?

Smoking is associated with being grown up and as long as young people see adults smoking and are exposed to advertising and other forms of tobacco promotion there will always be those who will be attracted to experimenting with tobacco. The next generation of smokers will be recruited from those who experiment.

While starting to smoke is something which we tend to attribute to young teenagers, children are aware of, and experiment with, cigarettes from an early age.[2,12] Pre-school children mimic adults smoking, just as they mimic other things they do, and some pre-school and primary school children do experiment with smoking.

The factors which influence whether or not young people start smoking regularly may be described in relation to:

- the individual
- the influence of the family
- friends and groups identified with
    school
    the community
    the wider environment.

To prevent young people from experimenting with tobacco and becoming regular smokers, we have to find out what we can about these influences and develop activities to address them. Figure 5 represents the process by which young people move from experimentation to regular smoking.

The factors identified above all play a part in deciding whether or not young people experiment with smoking and become regular smokers. Clearly, some of the factors are more important at certain ages than at others.

Figure 5. *Factors which influence regular smoking in young people*

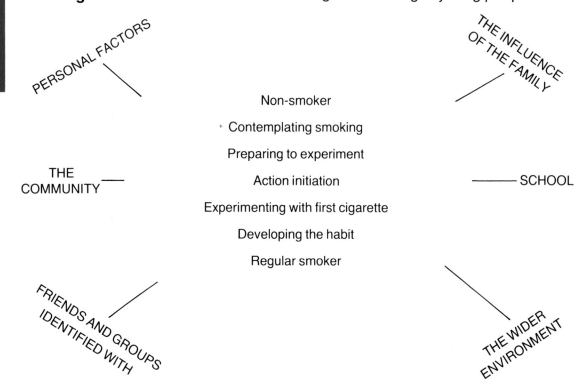

Personal factors

It is generally accepted that smoking is closely bound up with the developmental stage in adolescence when young people are experimenting with new behaviour and trying out new roles and experiences. Smoking may serve a number of purposes here including:

- testing adult authority
- coping with anxiety and frustration
- identifying with peers
- a rite of passage marking the transition from childhood experimentation to the 'status' of adult regular smoking
- meeting experimentation needs in adolescent development.

Research over the years has revealed that the following factors may contribute to young people becoming regular smokers:

Boys and girls

- Need to feel grown up or may have low self-esteem.
- Those under 11 think that smoking looks tough or grown up.
- Lack of knowledge and real understanding about health hazards.
- Lack of real understanding about how addictive smoking is.
- Overestimation of the number of their own age who smoke.
- Short-term gains seen as outweighing the health risks.
- Health risks not seen as personal to them.
- Coughs, sore throats and chest complaints not seen as being related to smoking.

The following table shows the results of a recent survey[35] showing the main factors, in order of importance, which help to predict the onset of smoking among 12–13-year-old boys and girls.

Table 3.
The main factors which help to predict the onset of smoking among 12-13 year-olds, in order of importance.

	Boys		Girls
1.	Having a best friend who smokes	1.	Having at least one parent who smokes
2.	Knowing at least one cigarette brand	2.	Having positive beliefs about what smoking will do for them, e.g. looking grown up, calming nerves, controlling weight, giving confidence, being enjoyable
3.	Having a favourite cigarette advertisement	3.	Knowing at least one cigarette brand
4.	Not knowing or accepting any of the health risks	4.	Having a best friend who smokes
5.	Having at least one parent who smokes	5.	Not knowing or accepting any of the health risks

It is important to recognise that different factors influence the smoking behaviour of boys and girls at different ages. Health education about smoking must take account of these gender differences where they are found.

Girls and young women

Twenty-five years ago there was little evidence of smoking among teenage girls. (Few studies were undertaken because the problem had not been identified.) Ten years ago smoking among this group was an established trend but at that time more teenage boys than teenage girls were smokers. Today, from the age of 14 to 17, more girls than boys are regular smokers, and by the time they are 15-year-olds 24 per cent of teenage girls smoke compared with 17 per cent of teenage boys.[12]

The reasons for this changing pattern are many and complex and may reflect:

– smoking among women becoming acceptable·

– changes in attitudes to smoking among women themselves
– the changing role of women in society
– deliberate targeting of women by the tobacco industry
– low-tar brands of cigarettes being targeted at women
– positive images of smoking in films and on television.

Girls

● Seem to be more affected by positive beliefs about what smoking will do for them.[35]

● Believe that smoking looks grown up, calms the nerves, gives confidence, can control weight and is enjoyable.[35]

The fact that girls mature earlier is also significant:[36]

● In England, girls who smoke attend discos more often than non-smokers where it appears they go in order to smoke as well as to listen to music and to dance.

28

- Girl smokers tend to have more male friends than those who are non-smokers, and the males tend to be older.
- Girls who smoke are more likely than non-smokers to use alcohol and other drugs.

What can we do?

By ensuring that young people follow a systematic curricular programme in health education with appropriate emphasis on smoking throughout their school careers, we can make a major contribution to the reduction of teenage smoking.

To be as effective as possible, teaching has to begin in primary school *before* the age when children begin to experiment with their first cigarette.

Special attention needs to be paid at the time of transfer to secondary school and, as in other aspects of the curriculum, good primary/secondary liaison helps planning for continuity and progression.

Like other components of health education provision, teaching about smoking should be developed in the form of a spiral curriculum. Different elements should be selected and presented to meet the individual needs of pupils, while laying the foundations for future work to meet their needs as they mature and pass through different developmental stages.

To be most effective, teaching about smoking should:

- be integrated with other areas of the whole curriculum
- have clearly defined objectives related to the specific needs of students
- have the reduction of smoking among young people as an important goal
- be student-centred and maximise learning through small groups, working in pairs, role play, etc.
- involve students in learning activities which allow them responsibility for their own decision-making

- allow gender differences in smoking behaviour to be addressed where appropriate.

Stress

When we help young people to cope with stress in their lives, the best starting point may be what stress means to them.[37,38] The need for young people to develop coping skills and social and interpersonal skills reinforces the notion of setting smoking education in a broad personal and social education context.

Advertising

Smoking education programmes should include information on the effects of advertising, but care must be taken that the work develops pupils' critical abilities and does not reinforce advertising messages. A useful approach may be to locate the work in the curriculum so that 'advertising' is the theme to be studied, and 'tobacco advertising' is featured as *an example* in lessons.

Gender

Some of the curricular initiatives which have been successful in helping to change the attitudes and behaviour of boys in relation to smoking have not achieved the same degree of success with girls. There are issues specific to young women and smoking which may have to be tackled in new ways if we are to be successful in reducing smoking.[39]

Because girls appear to have more positive beliefs about what smoking will do for them, e.g. make them appear more grown up, control weight, calm nerves, etc., we have to identify and acknowledge these beliefs and develop other ways for young women to explore and meet their needs. It is important for young women to explore how they feel about themselves, and about their relationships with others. As in any other work in health education the development of self-esteem, valuing oneself and thinking of oneself as someone capable of making decisions and taking control of one's own life, is essential.

It has been suggested that separate smoking education lessons for girls may be an effective strategy. Working in small groups and pairs and building social support networks have proved to be more effective in supporting young women in not taking up smoking. An examination of women's role in society, marketing techniques aimed at women, health risks specific to women, looking 'grown up' and in control *without* cigarettes, and coping with stress are all vital components of a smoking education programme aimed at girls and young women.

Section 4 of the manual looks in more detail at the issues surrounding school health education concerned with smoking, focusing specifically on context, content, delivery and timing. Examples and information about curricular materials and resources currently available are provided. Many of the curricular materials suggest ways of collecting information about pupils' knowledge about smoking, their attitudes towards it and their smoking behaviour. It is advisable to collect such information *before* planning your lessons. It is recommended that schools survey smoking behaviour among their pupils and use the information to develop and monitor programmes (see Section 6).

The influence of the family

Parents act as role models for their children and as such can reinforce healthy and unhealthy behaviour. Educating parents about smoking and the role of the family may be useful in helping to reduce teenage smoking, and smoking among parents themselves.[40] Research into the influence of the family on teenage smoking has revealed the following:

- Young people from homes where no adult smokes or from homes where parents are likely to disapprove of smoking are less likely to become regular smokers.[2,12]
- The smoking behaviour of older brothers and sisters can strongly influence younger children's smoking behaviour.[2,12]
- Boys are more likely to take up smoking if their fathers smoke.[41]
- The influence of parents seems to be strongest during the transition phase from experimenting with smoking to being a regular smoker.[42]
- Mothers seemingly become more permissive about smoking as their sons get older and this can reinforce the smoking behaviour of boys.[42]

Research has shown that parents' attitudes can be a powerful influence on adolescent smoking behaviour[43] and that, if parents express their disapproval of smoking, this influences young people in a positive way not to smoke, regardless of the parents' own smoking behaviour.

It appears that many parents are reluctant to tell their children not to smoke. This is either because they do not wish to appear hypocritical if they smoke themselves or because the change in public attitude has created an apathy among parents who may believe that the anti-smoking messages are clear, and they do not have to state the obvious to their children. There seems to be an overall trend towards greater parental permissiveness in relation to smoking[43] and in a recent study about a quarter of parents who claimed to be against their children's smoking were not perceived as being so by the children themselves.[42] It may be that there is still scope to recruit more parents into discouraging their children from smoking.

What can we do?

It is important that parents are involved in the development of a smoking programme through the PTA and any other means available, and that the programme has the full support of the school governors. Teachers

30

need to be aware that there may be sensitivities to some aspects of smoking education and special care is required with initiatives involving home–school links. Introducing parents to this national programme may be a useful way of putting the issue on the agenda. A smoking ban during parents' evenings or other meetings attended by parents can provide an opportunity to discuss the importance of the role of parents in preventing young people from smoking. Issues which might be raised with parents are:

- the hazards of smoking and passive smoking
- the risks to young people
- the importance of the role of the parents in smoking education
- how parental attitudes can influence young people's smoking
- how adolescent smoking behaviour may be seen in a general context of child development.

Parents can play a role in:

- helping to reduce the illegal sale of cigarettes to those under 16 (see Appendix iv)
- monitoring breaches in advertising codes for tobacco products, as they relate to young people (see Appendix ii)
- lobbying for smoke-free public transport and public places.

By liaising with your local health education unit (see the entry for your health authority in the telephone directory) you will also be able to make parents aware of other strategies which are planned or in use in your area to reduce smoking. Information about stop smoking classes could also be given, along with other help and support for parents trying to give up.

Friends and groups identified with

- Evidence suggests that the peak time when young people conform to group pressure is between the ages of 11 and 13. Young people are particularly vulnerable if the norm in the groups they belong to is to smoke.[41]
- Having a best friend who smokes is a strong predictor of adolescent smoking.[35]
- Young people who experiment with smoking often do so in a group.[34]
- Young people who become independent from home life at an early age and who may frequent fast food outlets, cafés, and shopping and amusement arcades may be at greater risk of becoming smokers.[27]

What can we do?

Some of the work undertaken in the curriculum programme will have specific relevance, e.g. communications skills, understanding peer pressure, refusal skills, coping mechanisms, etc. However, it is important to do the following:

- Be aware of other social reference groups outside the school and the activities young people are involved in.
- Ask yourself why children join a particular group; consider how the smoking norms develop in that group in the first place and see whether a healthy alternative can be offered.
- Liaise with other agencies running clubs, discos, sports events, etc. and promote the smoke-free message.
- Make information about 'SmokeBusters' clubs available to young people, but allow them to run their own club in a way that promotes their sense of ownership (see Appendix v).
- Lobby for smoke-free leisure centres, shopping arcades, swimming pools, discos,

fast food outlets and other places where young people gather.

Factors relating to school

- Education programmes about smoking and health have greater impact in schools which give a high profile to personal, social and health education in the curriculum,[44] and have a designated person to co-ordinate activities.

- Young people who do not like school and believe they are not achieving well are more likely to be smokers.[10,11]

- Adolescents who smoke often see smoking as a valid way of coping with stress in their lives.[37,38]

- Among young secondary school pupils whose parents don't know they smoke, school is the chosen venue for smoking if there are few penalties and restrictions.[27]

- There are great variations in smoking prevalence among schools, and smoking may have particular significance in individual institutions.[45-47]

- There is evidence of an association between smoking by headteachers and smoking prevalence among male pupils.[48]

- More pupils of both sexes smoke before and after leaving school if smoking is common among their teachers.[48]

- There may be an association between pupils' smoking and smoking among non-teaching staff.[49]

What can we do?

A formal school policy on smoking has an essential part to play in reducing smoking among young people and helping to establish non-smoking as the norm in our society.[50] An overview of policy development is given in Section 5. **Further advice on policy is available from the Health Education Authority, which is working towards establishing a negotiated smoke-free policy in educational establishments serving the 4–19 age range.**

Recent research[51] suggests that, where there is a formal written policy, health education provision tends to be more planned and systematic, especially where the policy stipulates the role of a co-ordinator for health education.

Because of the variation in prevalence among schools there is a need for schools to obtain data on smoking prevalence for their own use, so that they can time activities accurately and evaluate the effectiveness of their work. Section 6 of this manual provides information on conducting prevalence studies.

Factors relating to the community

- There is a growing body of evidence that cigarette advertising directly influences the decision to start smoking.[35]

- Cigarette advertising campaigns and promotions are often associated with fun, risk-taking and maturity, all of which appeal to young people.[52]

- Young people's main exposure to cigarette advertising is often through shop advertising and poster advertising.[53]

- Advertising aimed specifically at young women has emphasised slimness and sophistication, which is attractive to young teenage girls.[54]

- There are still many places in the community where young people are exposed to adults smoking and the tobacco smoke of others, e.g. foyers of swimming pools and leisure centres, sports centres, football stadiums, some carriages in trains and parts of some buses.

- Many shops and kiosks sell cigarettes illegally to young people under 16, and some sell individual cigarettes to young people.[47]

- The latest research findings[55] confirm that cigarette advertising is reinforcing under-age smoking.

32

What can we do?

- Find out about and undertake the activity promoted through the Parents Against Tobacco (PAT) campaign (see Appendix iv).

- Liaise with the district health authority and other groups working in the field of smoking prevention.

- Liaise with other community groups in trying to achieve non-smoking as the norm in as many places as possible, e.g. public halls, swimming pools, leisure centres, buses, etc.

- Help to monitor advertising, and notify COMATAS (see Appendix vi) of any breaches of the code of practice in relation to young people (see Appendix ii).

- Help to monitor the availability of cigarettes and their illegal sale to children.

- Develop links with youth, mass media and other organisations to discuss, debate and lobby for action in relation to advertising, illegal sales and the provision of smoke-free environments.

Young people themselves are often interested in community and environmental issues and can be guided to use their own initiative to become involved – writing letters, collecting signatures, monitoring advertising, etc.

Under the terms of the Children and Young Persons Act and the Protection of Children (Tobacco) Act 1986, it is illegal to sell cigarettes and other tobacco products to children under the age of 16. Local authorities are empowered to prosecute under Section 7 of the Children and Young Persons Act 1933 (amended). As this publication went to press, new legislation was under consideration (see Appendix iv).

Factors relating to the wider environment

- Young people's actions reflect the attitudes, values and norms of the society in which they live. If they see smoking as normal social behaviour with few restrictions on where or when it can take place, those who see smoking as conferring adult status may be encouraged to smoke.

- Showing smoking in a positive light in TV drama and in films in the cinema may reinforce positive beliefs about smoking and encourage young people to smoke.

- Raising the tax on cigarettes has been shown to reduce consumption in the past.[56]

What can we do?

Raise the issues over smoking and health with management teams, boards of governors and other influential groups and people, with the aim of gaining support and motivating them to lobby for change in:

- sales promotion
- advertising (see Appendix ii)
- taxation (see Appendix iii)
- wider provision of smoke-free environments (for addresses of groups who can help, see Appendix vi).

To smoke or not to smoke?

In devising strategies and activities for an effective smoking education programme it is useful to look at four key questions that young people might ask themselves when making decisions about smoking:[57]

1. Is the threat to health serious?

Upper primary school children are much less likely to know about the dangers to health from smoking than secondary children. They may mention lung cancer but do not have any idea of what it really is.

It is important to teach an understanding of the health risks of smoking and their seriousness at about age 9, when children are beginning to experiment with their first cigarette out of curiosity.

2. Is the threat personal to me?

Accepting the threat of disease and ill-health which might develop in the future is a difficult concept for young people, especially when they can see adults, who appear to be healthy, smoking. Like adults, children quickly learn to rationalise their smoking behaviour.

Using techniques to show the immediate effects of carbon monoxide, nicotine and tar on the body can demonstrate just how harmful smoking can be, and may allow young people to see that the threat is personal to them. This work can be developed into looking at the short-term health risks and exploring health behaviour.

3. What will I lose by deciding to give up smoking?

Young people may hear, understand and accept the message about being a non-smoker, but all the social factors from their immediate surroundings and the wider environment can militate against taking the decision not to smoke. Influences such as smoking within the family, cigarette advertising, and film and television images of smoking may be conducive to a positive set of values and perceived benefits, e.g.

Smoking - looks grown up
 - gives confidence
 - calms nerves
 - is friendly and sociable
 - helps you to relax
 - helps you to concentrate
 - keeps weight down
 - looks sophisticated
 - looks tough

Deciding to stop smoking involves accepting the loss of the perceived benefits of smoking. This can mean fear of alienation from friends and family if they are smokers. It can also mean anxiety about the ability to cope with situations without cigarettes.

Techniques which can be usefully employed in trying to counter these problems are:

1. A 'whole family' approach to smoking education.
2. Helping children to be non-smokers without losing their friends.
3. Using discussion to seek out the reasons why children smoke. Helping them to find other ways of coping with stress, weight, etc. Drawing on the coping skills of non-smokers in the same situation.

4. What will I gain by deciding to stop smoking?

The losses perceived by not smoking often prevent positive decisions about giving up smoking from being taken. However, the process of assessing the gains can go some way towards stopping smoking appearing more attractive.

It is important therefore to discover the gains from being a non-smoker which are relevant to young people. A positive message is better than a negative one. Future gains and approaches dealing with sports performance may not be relevant to all children, therefore we need to know more about what they would personally value. Psychologically, it is helpful to avoid the term 'giving up' smoking. 'Stopping' smoking or 'breaking free' from the habit are suitable alternatives.

Girls, more than boys, seem to hold positive beliefs about what smoking will do for them.

Even if parents are smokers their disapproval of their child smoking can have a positive effect.

Smoking and the Curriculum

- The personal, social and health education context

The National Curriculum

Age, stage and development

Co-ordination

Curriculum audit

Content, delivery and timing

The teacher's role

What can schools do?

The personal, social and health education context

Health education is taught in virtually all primary and secondary schools in this country, usually as topic work in the primary sector and as part of science, home economics, physical education, and personal and social education (PSE) in the secondary sector.

PSE allows for a focus on the acquisition of health-related skills such as communication, decision-making, coping with peer group pressure, assertiveness, etc. Co-ordination is an important feature of such work. Looking across the curriculum, it is important that omissions are noted and redressed, unhelpful duplication avoided and opportunities to reinforce learning experiences taken.

Form tutors are sometimes required to deliver health education as part of a pastoral or tutorial programme in secondary schools. This works well in many cases, although there can be problems. Teachers who have not received specific health education INSET may perceive themselves as lacking the knowledge, skills and confidence to teach health education. Time can be an issue, the allocation for tutorial periods often being too short to undertake health education work productively, especially when registration and other administrative duties have to be completed in the same period.

While it is possible to teach health education in a variety of ways, it has proved *most* effective in schools where adequate timetabled provision has been made for it within subject areas and within separate courses of PSE.

This allows teachers to address any gaps in provision arising in the subject bases or

36

through 'options'. It also allows time and space for children to bring together and make sense of the knowledge and skills gained in different subject areas.

The National Curriculum

Health education is not a separately identified foundation subject within the National Curriculum, but aspects of health education appear within the Statutory Orders for Science[58] and other foundation subjects and it is a major cross-curricular theme identified by the National Curriculum Council.[59]

Whatever the organisational pattern chosen for the teaching of the curriculum, effective health education:

- has to be delivered in a way relevant to the particular needs of pupils
- embodies the main areas of experience agreed to be important
- shows continuity and progression from age 5–16.

Smoking education is referred to specifically in the Statutory Order for Science in the National Curriculum:[58]

Attainment Target 3, Processes of Life includes the following requirements at Levels 4 and 6.

Level 4
Pupils should 'know about the factors which contribute to good health and body maintenance, including the defence systems of the body, balanced diet, oral hygiene and avoidance of harmful substances such as tobacco, alcohol and other drugs'.

Level 6
Pupils should 'understand the risks of alcohol, solvent and drug abuse and how they affect body processes'.

Attainment targets within English, Maths and Technology can be met through smoking education. For example:

Maths – Attainment Targets 12, 13 and 14 'Handling data'.
Level 5 – construct and interpret a pie chart from a collection of data with a few variables interpret pie charts already prepared in journals and newspapers.
English – Attainment Targets 1, 2 and 3 – listening and speaking allows pupils to discuss smoking issues.
Technology – some aspects of health and safety come under this area – smoking education could be developed under Level 9 – how manufacturers must provide information to users of products.

Other aspects of the National Curriculum pertain to smoking education. For example, historical aspects of tobacco, geography and environmental concerns, physical education and cardiovascular appraisal, all play a part in the planned and co-ordinated programme.

Guidance from the National Curriculum Council

Schools have already received from the National Curriculum Council *Curriculum Guidance 5: Health Education*[59] which deals in some detail with the curriculum organisation and curriculum content for nine components at each key stage and teaching and learning styles. Smoking education is featured within the component theme entitled 'Substance use and misuse'. It is also used as an exemplar to illustrate the links between components of health education and with National Curriculum subjects. *This document is essential reading.*

Age, stage and development

Primary school

Age 4–8

Recent research into perceptions of health among primary school children has shown that from age 4–8 children's perceptions about what they can do to make themselves healthy revolve around positive ideas, principally about food, exercise and play.[60,61]

Age 8–9

By age 8–9 the children in the study were beginning to mention items which could have a negative effect on health and began to recognise that substances could be harmful. Although there was a large increase in the number of children saying that cigarettes could be harmful, there was greater mention of heroin and hard drugs. The research also revealed that negative instructions such as 'don't do this' had little impact on children at this stage.

Age 10–11

At age 10–11, the time when many children experiment with a first cigarette, the number of times cigarettes were mentioned as being harmful to health was considerably less than with the 8–9 age group. This could reflect the fact that, at the time when experimentation takes place, there is a shift to a more positive attitude to smoking. It could also reflect the fact that seeing adults smoke and cigarettes advertised gives mixed messages which cause confusion about the dangers to health and anxiety about parents who are smokers.

At age 10 the children seem to think that it is someone else's responsibility to keep them safe; by age 11 they are beginning to realise that they have some degree of responsibility for looking after themselves.

The development of understanding about the long-term dangers of substances such as alcohol and tobacco, and understanding about the possible future outcome of present actions, begins to emerge at age 10, but only in a few children. However, by about age 11 their perceptions of the health of adults reveal that children are beginning to understand the concept of lifestyle in relation to health.

The majority of children in the investigation, while revealing a perception of the overall drug scene as bad, do not place coffee, alcohol and cigarettes within that context.

A spiral curriculum which revisits the subject of smoking, and meets the needs of the pupils throughout their school careers, provides an ideal home for smoking education.

The smoking component should begin at about age 9 when children are beginning to understand the harmful nature of substances and are often about to experiment with a first cigarette. However, there are other aspects of smoking education which begin at an earlier age – these would include work on friendships, body image and valuing themselves. If primary pupils themselves raise

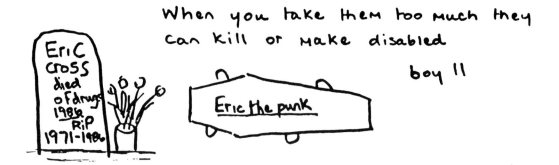

the issue of smoking at an earlier stage, teachers can use the opportunity to explore the issues raised with the individual and, where appropriate, with the class.

Secondary school

Recent research has revealed that overall 52 per cent of secondary pupils remembered having a lesson about smoking. However, only 29 per cent of first-year pupils recalled lessons about smoking compared with 53 per cent of third-year pupils and 65 per cent of fifth-year pupils in the secondary school.[62]

The percentage of secondary pupils who recalled receiving health education lessons on smoking in the last year was as follows:

Year 1 (Y7)	29%
Year 2 (Y8)	43%
Year 3 (Y9)	53%
Year 4 (Y10)	60%
Year 5 (Y11)	65%

(*Source:* OPCS)[62]

It is important that the work undertaken in primary school continues to develop in the form of a spiral curriculum so that all pupils have smoking education throughout their secondary careers.

As the transition from primary to secondary school is a key time for experimenting with smoking, smoking education is essential for all pupils and should be addressed early in that school year.

Ability

A range of achievement may be expected of pupils within teaching groups of any given age. The linking of chronological age to an assumed stage of development may offer a general formula for a smoking education curriculum, but classroom practice must allow for variations in young people's abilities.

Therefore teachers need to adopt a flexible approach in their detailed planning of schemes of work, and it can be assumed that their professional judgement and personal knowledge of pupils are as worthwhile as the advice of experts in smoking education.

Co-ordination

It is clear that a health education programme for smoking has a home in the whole curriculum, and a specified location within the science curriculum. What may not be so clear is that aspects of science within the National Curriculum[58] may be taught by non-scientists, and in subjects other than 'science' on the timetable. The attainment targets may be reached through a range of different organisational patterns:

1. Identifying areas of shared interest with other subjects outside science.
2. Teaching course modules by using a team of teachers with particular expertise or interest.

3. Integrating components to form *topics* of study.

The mechanics of timetabling, teaching expertise, pupils' option choices for years 10 and 11 in the secondary school are all issues which may impinge on the provision of smoking education. However, it is co-ordination which emerges as the crucial factor.

The issue of co-ordination of health education is addressed in the National Curriculum Council publication *Curriculum Guidance 5: Health Education.*[59]

Many valuable lessons have already been gleaned from teachers responsible for co-ordinating health education across the curriculum. Some of these are presented in the following section. Readers are also advised to familiarise themselves with the relevant INSET materials produced by the National Curriculum Council.

Curriculum audit

Enquiry grids can be used to carry out a curriculum audit in order to establish what health education, including smoking education, is going on and where. This approach can provide a useful snapshot of the curriculum, but it is important to remember the following:

1. It is vitally important that teaching staff understand precisely what they are being asked and why; an insensitive enquiry may give an inaccurate picture of the curriculum.

2. A grid can reveal a lot about content, but the processes being used are less easy to identify. Method is just as important as content in determining effective lessons in smoking education. The gathering of this information also needs to be approached with sensitivity.

3. A completed grid is just a starting point – it helps to set the agenda for co-ordination across the curriculum but it will need updating to take account of changes in curricula and staff. Evaluation is an essential feature of a curriculum audit. It is important to consider questions such as:

- Does every pupil have access to a broad and balanced health education curriculum?
- What changes may be needed to support strengths and overcome weaknesses?
- How far have the objectives been met?
- How can the programme be accelerated or slowed down to meet the needs of the children?

4. There may be obstacles to adopting smoking education.

- It is not perceived as being important.
- It is not considered relevant to basic educational skills.
- It is perceived as an unwelcome addition to an already overcrowded curriculum (and an already overburdened teacher!).
- It is seen as a non-examinable topic, more concerned with exploring feelings than acquiring knowledge.
- It may not be seen by a teacher as part of her role.

People who encounter such obstacles may begin to find solutions by highlighting common core objectives to show that health education can be integrated with basic educational skills in other subject disciplines. By integrating elements of a smoking programme with other subject areas, the amount of health education can be increased while reducing the demand on time in the curriculum.

Content, delivery and timing

The following represents a distillation of key findings and recommendations from research.[39,60,61,63-71]

40

Content

Ideally, health education about smoking should include the following:

- **Information about the short-term health effects and the consequences of smoking.** This needs to be presented in a relevant and stimulating way and within a wider context, as information in isolation is ineffective.

- **Exploration of social influences to smoke** particularly in relation to peers, parents and the media.

- **Correction of adolescents' overestimation** of the number smoking in their age group, so that they are aware that smokers are a minority.

- **Development of skills in decision-making**, problem-solving and resisting unwanted pressure from others.

- **Development of coping strategies** to replace cigarette smoking; lessons designed to meet the different needs of boys and girls in relation to their attitudes to smoking and their smoking behaviour – young children do not even begin to incorporate them into their thinking before the age of 8.

- **A positive approach** emphasising what young children can do to be healthy may be more effective. Negative health instructions seem to have little impact.

Delivery

The active participation of pupils makes their smoking education more effective.

- One effective method is to involve peers as leaders or assistants, with the teacher retaining overall responsibility for the lessons. Peer leaders operate best when they receive training from the teacher and support for the task. There are implications for training teachers.

- The active involvement of parents is most desirable before the age of 11–12. For older children, involvement of the parents can even be counterproductive. Engaging parents' *support* to express disapproval and helping them to improve their skills in communicating with teenage children is worthwhile, although this aspect needs further research.

- Health education about smoking seems to be effective whether it is done as a separate topic or as part of a more general programme of health education as long as the smoking component receives adequate attention (see Timing below).

- Teacher training is essential: the content should relate closely to the proposed learning activities with the emphasis on active learning, skills training, interaction in peer groups and with peer assistants.

Timing

- **As a minimum, concentrate on teaching pupils who are at the age where the risk of onset of smoking is greatest.**

  The greatest effort should be made one to three years prior to the steepest onset of regular smoking. In England the national data indicate this to be 11–13 years of age; however, we recommend that schools conduct their own prevalence surveys to confirm this.

- **Use a spiral curriculum approach that takes account of children's current knowledge and their stage of development.**

  Address understanding and skills as well as recall of factual information. The main focus will tend to be on different aspects at the appropriate stages of pupils' development. For example, prior to estimated age of onset, health information/formation of attitudes may be emphasised; at estimated age of onset, managing social influences may take precedence. Later reinforcement or so-called 'booster' sessions may involve further work about health information/ social influences. It has been suggested that a further stage might be concerned with early cessation, i.e. providing help both inside and outside school for those pupils who wish to stop smoking. More research is needed into the effectiveness of this type of work.

● **Ideally, teaching should begin before the age when we think children start to experiment with tobacco and continue through all school years.**

Some experts have advised that, if it is possible, schools should plan to impart appropriate health education about smoking before the age when children are beginning to experiment in earnest and that it should continue through all school years. We know from recent research[12] that 8 per cent of children aged 9 have tried smoking.

● Some examples of materials that may be incorporated within a spiral curriculum are featured on pages 41–45.

My Body Project

Age range 7–11

Content

Teachers' guide, pupils' cards; cross-curricular project clearly mapped for National Curriculum attainment targets.

Developed by the Health Education Authority

Available from:

Heinemann Educational Books Halley Court Jordan Hill Oxford OX2 8EJ

Hooked

Age range 9+

Content

Board game, encourages understanding of information, attitudes and issues which affect smoking behaviour

Developed by the Cancer Research Campaign

Available from:

TACADE
1 Hulme Place
The Crescent
Salford M5 4QA

C932

Age range 9–10

Content

Children's story book, parents' leaflet, teachers' plan for follow-up work

Developed by the Cancer Research Campaign

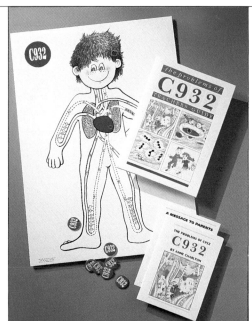

Available from:

Nottingham
Educational Supplies
17 Ludlow Hill Road
West Bridgford
Nottingham NG2 6HD

Terminal Boredom

Age range 11–12

Content

Video, colour, 15 mins. Animation/live action. Smoking seen from 23rd century school lesson. Teachers' notes.

Developed by the Health Education Authority

Available from:

Health Education Authority Hamilton House Mabledon Place London WC1H 9TX

NEW

Smoking and Pollution

Age range 11–12

Content

Free package, teachers' guide, pupils' workbook, parents' leaflet

Developed by the Health Education Authority

Available from:

Health Education Authority Hamilton House Mabledon Place London WC1H 9TX

44

Smoking and Me

Age range 12–13

Content

Teachers' guide to five lessons, material for peer-group learning, encourages discussion, role play and skill development

Developed by the Health Education Authority

Available from:

Health Education Authority
Hamilton House
Mabledon Place
London WC1H 9TX

NEW

Seven Ages of Moron

Age range 13–14

Content

Video, colour 23 mins. Mel Smith/Griff Rhys-Jones look at stages in a smoker's life, questions glamour of smoking

Developed by the Cancer Research Campaign

Available from:

Cancer Research Campaign
2 Carlton House Terrace
London SW1Y 6AR

Packing It In?

Age range 15+

Content

Set of guidelines, plans for stopping smoking geared to nine types of young smoker: pleasure-time/ confidence/sensation/ comfort/concentration/ social-confidence/keep going/automatic/ addicted

Developed by the Cancer Research Campaign

Available from:

TACADE
1 Hulme Place
The Crescent
Salford M5 4QA

45

Adolescent Smoking Cessation in Schools

Age range 15+

Content

Teachers' guide on how to organize and run a school stop smoking group.
  Six-week course.

Developed by the Ulster Cancer Foundation/ASH Northern Ireland

Available from:

Ulster Cancer Foundation
40–42 Eglantine Avenue
Belfast BT9 6DX

The teacher's role

To see a decline in young people's smoking, we must adopt an approach which will embrace all the factors we have identified as influencing smoking behaviour: individual factors, family, groups, school, community and the wider environment. To be successful we must support young people in staying smoke-free in as many ways as we can, and promote non-smoking as the norm in our society. The aim is to enable young people to make a self-empowered choice about smoking in an environment that is supportive of being smoke-free. There is a place for both educational and preventive approaches within the context of health education related to smoking. Tones[72] argues that personal and social education *per se* is the more significant factor since, in principle, it obviates the need for preventive health education, other than provision of basic information (for a full discussion of this theme, see B.K. Tones).[73,74]

Figure 6 shows an all-embracing approach to school health promotion, building on and complementing work undertaken in PSE.

Figure 6 illustrates certain issues:

Figure 6. *The relative roles of PSE and health education in schools health promo*

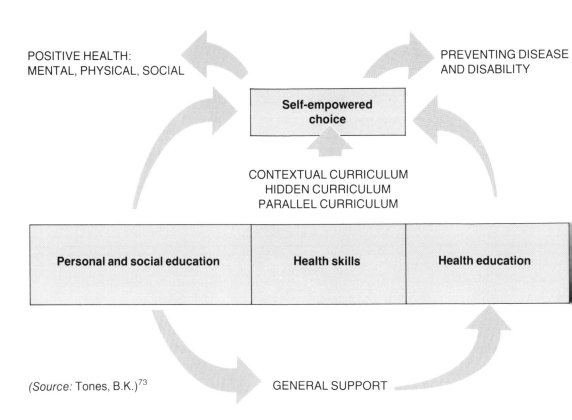

(Source: Tones, B.K.)[73]

1. Effective PSE and health education depend on co-ordination which involves subjects across the whole curriculum (contextual curriculum).

2. Health education is strengthened by the programme in PSE largely as a result of the overall contribution to self-esteem and values clarification which PSE can make.

3. There is an area of overlap – health skills – where PSE can be applied to specific health issues such as smoking, e.g. life-skills teaching to help pupils resist social pressure to smoke.

4. There are influences coming from the 'hidden curriculum' operating in the school (relationships, atmosphere, messages about health, etc.).

5. There are influences ('parallel curriculum' in the model) outside school which affect pupils' behaviour both in and out of school (family, groups, community, wider environment, etc.).

6. The goal is to foster self-empowered decision-making.

7. PSE has an important role in raising consciousness about socio-environmental influences on health.

What can teachers do?

- Support curriculum development in smoking education.

- Support and become actively involved in promoting, developing and operating the school smoking policy.

- Define training needs and make them known.

- Support community initiatives to reduce smoking.

- Liaise with other professionals sharing the same goal.

- Provide an adult role model of non-smoking.

What can schools do?

- Make sure that governors, parents, teachers and all those working in, or using, school premises and facilities are aware of the issues relating to smoking, health and young people.

- Enlist the full support of the local education and health authority(ies).

- Consult with the groups identified above, to work towards negotiating and implementing a formal school policy on smoking which covers pupils and all those using, or working on, school premises, school grounds, school outings and trips.

- Ensure that personal, social and health education has a secure place in the curriculum and that there is smoking education for all pupils, co-ordinated across the curriculum.

- Make sure that there is a designated person responsible for co-ordinating health education in the school and that this responsibility is reflected in the salary incentive allowance.

- Provide in-service training for staff and others relating to the smoking programme.

- Involve family and the wider community in the programme.

- Become actively involved with outside agencies with similar goals for health.

- Develop the image of the school as one which promotes health and does not give conflicting messages to pupils.

- Work towards becoming completely smoke-free.

Implications for action

- Since we know that children as young as 9 are trying smoking and experimentation with smoking peaks at age 11–14, an extensive cross-curricular approach spanning primary and secondary school is required.

    Education *before* as well as during the years when young people begin to

47

48

experiment with smoking has been shown to have a positive effect on knowledge and behaviour.[75]

- Surveys and class activities have a key part to play in identifying attitudes to smoking, smoking behaviour and smoking prevalence.

- Buying cigarettes is an early part of smoking behaviour and it is important that the law forbidding the sale of cigarettes to those under 16 is enforced (see Appendix iv).

- It is important to:
  - make young people aware of the immediate dangers of smoking
  - reduce opportunities to smoke at school and elsewhere
  - create an environment where non-smoking is the norm and young people are not exposed to adult smoking
  - reduce the confusion caused by conflicting messages about smoking (young people are exposed to health warnings and health campaigns about the dangers of smoking, while at the same time cigarettes are readily available and widely advertised, and many adults still smoke).

Towards an Effective School Smoking Policy: An Overview

Smoking by teachers

Smoking by pupils

Teachers' attitudes to smoking at school

Towards an effective policy

Implementing a smoke-free school policy: a checklist

Effective disciplinary procedures

Note: Teacher trade unions, school governor associations, headteachers' associations, the Department of Education & Science and the Department of Health are working together with the HEA to make implementation guidelines available to schools. A policy implementation manual is in preparation.

Smoking by teachers

Research into smoking by teachers suggests that about one in six of the profession smoke tobacco[76,77] and that a large majority of schools allow teachers to smoke in the staff room.

- Over half of secondary schools in England allow pupils to talk to teachers at the staff room door.[78]

- Approximately one in three schools allow teachers to invite pupils into the staff room.[79]

- Where there is awareness of the existence of a policy there may yet be confusion about the content.[80]

- Only 11 per cent of primary schools and 33 per cent of secondary schools have any form of written policy.[51]

- Some teachers do not feel that their school smoking policy restricts smoking in the staff room.[78]

- Up to 17 per cent of schools allow teachers to smoke in front of pupils particularly on school outings.[51]

From this evidence it appears that many pupils have ample opportunity to observe their teachers smoking.

Smoking by pupils

Ninety-six per cent of schools appear to have a policy on pupils smoking[44], although it may not be in written form. Less than one in 20 schools permit smoking by pupils, and where they do, it is usually restricted to sixth formers in designated areas.[44,51]

No smoking v designated smoking areas

In one study, it was found that the proportion of smokers and the average number of cigarettes smoked per day were both considerably lower in schools where pupils were forbidden to smoke, compared to those where designated smoking areas were provided.[81]

Encouraging the establishment of smoking policies in schools by negotiation remains an important objective of the national programme.

Teachers' attitudes to smoking at school

Teachers' knowledge and attitudes about smoking are likely to determine their smoking behaviour at school, the way they detect and respond to pupils smoking, and their effectiveness as health educators. A recent Welsh survey[80] of teachers' opinions revealed that:

- Most teachers (71 per cent) thought that their personal example was an important influence on pupils' smoking behaviour.
- Most teachers (76 per cent) thought that they should actively persuade pupils not to smoke.
- Most teachers (76 per cent) wanted a staff smoking policy discussed and established in their school.
- Most teachers (87%) wanted the right to use a staff room free from smoke.

At present many children are exposed to teachers and older pupils smoking on school premises. This has the effect of devaluing education about smoking and health. Children themselves complain that it is hypocrisy for teachers to offer health education to young people and then light up a cigarette as soon as the bell goes.[27,82]

Towards an effective policy

To be effective a formal school policy on smoking should address the following:

- smoking in school buildings
- smoking in school grounds
- smoking on school outings and trips
- smoking among pupils
- smoking among teaching and non-teaching staff
- smoking among visitors and all who use the facilities
- smoking education in the curriculum for all pupils.

The long-term aim should be to work towards the voluntary elimination of smoking on a 24-hour basis.

Rationale

The reasons for having a formal written policy on smoking may be stated as follows:

- It is a health and safety issue for teaching and non-teaching staff.
- Smoking is the single most preventable cause of premature death and ill-health in our society.
- Medical and scientific experts have documented the hazards to health presented by passive smoking.
- Everyone has the right to breathe clean air and non-smokers are in the majority.
- Smoking among teachers reinforces the idea of smoking being associated with maturity.

- School is an important setting for educating young people about healthy behaviour.

- Pupils themselves see the hypocrisy of teachers who smoke being involved in health education.

- School policies and practices influence pupils' behaviour.

- The school environment has a major role to play in working towards non-smoking being seen as the norm in society.

School policies on smoking give pupils the message that smoking creates health problems for smokers and non-smokers, that non-smoking represents the norm in society and that it receives support from the school and the staff.

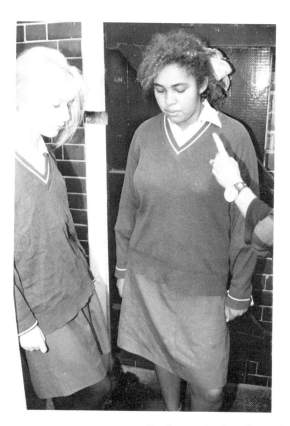 

Pupils perceive it as hypocrisy when teachers are smokers.

52

Implementing a school policy on smoking: a checklist

A policy on smoking should apply to all adults and young people who use the school premises. Research literature[50,64] suggests that the following factors contribute to the successful implementation of a school smoking policy which may reduce the incidence of smoking among pupils. For convenience they are presented in a checklist of ten points.

- Headteachers, senior staff and school governors communicate that they attach great importance to the development and implementation of a school smoking policy.

- All staff, pupils and non-teaching staff are fully aware of the reasons for having a smoking policy.

- Those involved in negotiating, developing and implementing the policy consult with all teaching and non-teaching staff, professional bodies and unions, and communicate the method by which the policy will be achieved and the arrangements for review and update.

- Parents and those in the community using school premises or facilities are involved.

- Careful consideration is given to the timing of implementation and review phases. (Policy implementation at the start of the academic year is favourable as it avoids problems surrounding changes in mid year.)

- The adopted policy is regarded as fair, realistic and well enforced. It is seen to address concerns, and to avoid over-complicated components which are impossible to enforce.

- The policy takes the form of a written statement where all aspects are carefully delineated:
  - formal disciplinary procedures
  - involvement by all teachers in the above

  - written schemes of work for the curriculum with optimal curriculum continuity, record-keeping, primary/secondary liaison.

- The policy is constantly given a high profile and the related communication with pupils is reinforced through assemblies, registration and school diaries.

- Teachers adopt disciplinary procedures which are known to be most effective, e.g. involving parents. (The emphasis may best be placed on valuing health rather than on addressing major disciplinary codes that require personnel and time to be fully enforced. On-site stop smoking classes might be considered as a useful alternative to punitive measures.)

- The policy encompasses compliance by teachers and non-teaching staff which derives from a co-operative agreement with management. Professional and responsible approaches seem to work best. All staff work to develop the image of the school as one which promotes health and avoids giving conflicting messages to pupils.

Effective disciplinary procedures

Existing evidence suggests that the most effective disciplinary procedures for pupils who smoke are:[83]

- quiet but firm reprimands or discussions
- involvement of parents
- loss of rewards or privileges
- increased supervision administered fairly and consistently.

It is important that all staff are clear about the procedures and are committed to applying them consistently. Lack of commitment by individual teachers in dealing with smoking by pupils will only serve to undermine the school's smoking policy.[78]

School-based Prevalence Surveys

Why school surveys are needed

How you can use the results

When and how to conduct surveys

Smoking questionnaire

Why school surveys are needed

Agencies like the OPCS and the Health Education Authority provide national data about smoking prevalence which give an overall picture of the numbers of young people who are smoking. However, it is important to remember that at local level there are variations between individual schools. Research has already shown this to be the case.[45] We therefore recommend that schools undertake their own prevalence surveys with pupils of 11 years of age and over.

How you can use the results

A study of prevalence can be undertaken simply and can pay great dividends. The results can provide each school with:

- a baseline from which to monitor the effectiveness of its own programme
- a measure of the prevalence of smoking among pupils
- information to help with curriculum planning and the timing of specific components
- data that can be used in pupils' own school work in a variety of ways.

When and how to conduct surveys

Prevalence can be determined by administering a questionnaire. The questionnaire on page 55 is reproduced with the kind permission of Dr Anne Charlton and the Cancer Research Campaign, and may be photocopied for use in schools. Responses can be analysed by hand or by computer.

Schools have approached surveys in different ways. One method is to carry out the survey before smoking education is undertaken and then to repeat it during or after the programme. Another method is to survey pupils at ages 11, 13 and 15 and to repeat the study every two years, thus tracking prevalence in the same pupils throughout their school career. If you have never conducted a prevalence survey in your school before, you may decide that your first study should cover *all age groups* before you make any further decisions about this.

It is clearly desirable to share the aims of the survey with the pupils from the outset. In addition, in order to increase the accuracy of the pupils' responses to the questionnaire, we recommend that three important rules are observed.

1. Administer the questionnaire to whole classes, under the supervision of a teacher.

2. Tell pupils *not* to write their names on the form because the results are to remain anonymous – explain clearly that nobody will know who has answered the questions.

3. Ask the children to seal their completed questionnaires in plain envelopes before collection.

Smoking questionnaire

Please do not write your name. This is not a test and will not be marked. Please answer all the questions.

Please take no notice of the little numbers beside the boxes or in the margins. They are just there to help us.

Nobody will know who answered these questions.

1. I am a ☐ boy ☐ girl Please tick 1

2
3
2. My age is ___ years ___ months 4
5

3. I go to _____ 6
Please write the name of your 7
school or college

4. If you are at college, what course are you studying at present? 8
_____ 9

5. I am in _____ 10
Please write the name of your 11
form, class or year

12
6. Today's date is _____ 13
14
15
16
17

7. Please read the following statements carefully and tick the space which best describes you.

Tick <u>one space</u> only.

(a) I have never smoked a cigarette. 1	
(b) I have only ever tried smoking once. 2	
(c) I used to smoke sometimes, but I don't now. 3	
(d) I smoke sometimes, but I don't smoke as much as one cigarette. 4	
(e) I usually smoke between one and six cigarettes a week. 5	
(f) I usually smoke more than six cigarettes a week. 6	

18

8. For each of these two questions, write the number in the box. If you haven't smoked any cigarettes, write 0 in the boxes.

(a) <u>Since this time yesterday,</u> how many cigarettes have you smoked? ☐☐ 19 / 20

(b) <u>Since this time last week,</u> how many cigarettes have you smoked? ☐☐ 21 / 22 / 23

9. How old were you the first time you tried smoking a cigarette, even if it was only a puff or two? ☐

<u>Please write in the box your age when you first tried smoking. If you have never tried smoking, write 0 in the box.</u> 24 / 25

10. Do you think you will smoke when you leave school or college for good?

	1	2	3	
<u>Please tick one box</u>	yes	no	don't know	26

Objectives of the National Programme

- To provide all 11–13-year-olds with the motivation, knowledge and skills to resist the pressure to smoke through mass media and publicity campaigns, and the provision of curricular and other relevant materials.

- To make similar provision for the 9–10 age group and the 14–19 age group later in the programme.

- To develop stop smoking techniques for teenagers where appropriate.

- To conduct research to inform the planning and development of the programme and monitor its progress and success.

- To facilitate a simple approach for schools to survey smoking among teenagers, and use the information to plan, develop and monitor their strategy to reduce teenage smoking.

- To seek continuous feedback on progress at local level and disseminate strategies through conferences, etc.

- To support educational and community activities aimed at substantially reducing illegal sales of tobacco to children under 16.

- To work towards establishing a negotiated smoke-free policy in educational establishments serving the 4–19 age range.

Advertising

Children are aware of advertisements from an early age. Like adults they see tobacco and cigarette advertisements on billboards and shop fronts in the street, in newspapers and magazines, and watch tobacco-sponsored sport on TV or at road or air shows.

Several studies have shown that children are most aware of, and likely to smoke, the most heavily advertised brands, and one large Australian study found that approval of cigarette advertisements came second after having friends who smoked as the best indicator of whether or not a child would subsequently smoke.

The government seeks to protect children from exposure to cigarette and other tobacco advertising by means of the advertising code on tobacco and by voluntary agreements between the tobacco companies and the Minister for Health, and between the Tobacco Advisory Council and the Minister for Sport. These regulate the nature of cigarette and tobacco adverts, the size and location of billboards and other forms of advertising, the use of health warnings and how much money can be spent on advertising and other forms of promotional activity.

Copies of the Voluntary Agreement on Tobacco Products, Advertising and Promotion, and Health Warnings are available from: The Secretary, COMATAS, 6th Floor, Clements House, Gresham Street, London EC2V 7DN.

Voluntary Agreement on Tobacco Products, Advertising and Promotion, and Health Warnings, April 1986

The relevant clauses relating to children and tobacco advertising are as follows:

1.9 There will be no static outdoor cigarette and hand-rolling tobacco brand advertising (excluding signs on retail premises) in close proximity to and clearly visible and identifiable from within buildings or boundaries of schools, places of education or playgrounds predominantly used by young people under 18 years of age, nor adjacent to entrances and exits or the pavements forming the boundaries to such schools, places of education and playgrounds.

1.12 When the companies advertise other goods or services with the same name or similar name to that of a tobacco product, the advertisement will be designed in such a way that the particular goods or services being advertised are clearly identified and such goods or services will not have a greater appeal to persons under 18 years of age than to the adult population as a whole.

1.13 The companies will endeavour to ensure that 'other goods' bearing tobacco brand names or designs in a manner having the effect of directly associating the 'other goods' with a tobacco product are not produced for, sold or given away to persons under the age of 18. In fulfilling this responsibility the companies will exercise special care to avoid cigarette brand advertising or logos on material which may be given away or sold to such young people at sponsored or promotional events such as road shows, air shows or similar occasions when vehicles bearing advertising material may be put on display. The companies will actively discourage the manufacturers of 'other goods' likely to have special appeal to such young people from associating their products with tobacco brand names or designs.

1.14 The industry will spend about £1 million per annum on conducting a campaign with the retail trade at points of retail sale and in the media to encourage support for the law prohibiting the sale of cigarettes to children under 16. Notices on the law will be made extensively available for display by the retail trade and for fixing to automatic vending machines by their operators.

1.18 No advertising of cigarette or hand-rolling tobacco brands will be placed in magazines or periodicals published in their own right when it is apparent that at the time the advertisement is placed the publication has a female readership of more than 200,000 and more than 33 per cent of those female readers are aged 15–24. For established magazines the average of the previous four quarterly reports of the national readership survey will be the basis on which such a decision is taken.

Extract from the British Code of Advertising Practice

Appendix 1. Advertising of Cigarettes, of the Components of Manufactured Cigarettes and of Hand-rolling Tobacco

1.9 The essence of the code is that advertisements should not seek to encourage people, particularly the young, to start smoking or, if they are already smokers, to increase the level of smoking, or to smoke to excess; and should not exploit those who are especially vulnerable, in particular young people and those who suffer from any physical, mental or social handicap.

2.12 No advertisement should appear in any publication directed wholly or mainly at young people.

2.13 Advertisements should not feature heroes of the young.

3.3 *Youth rules.* In interpreting the rules in relation to youth, advertisers should take special care not to address their advertisements particularly to young people, even where there is no suggestion that the product is for their consumption, e.g. where it is intended as a present for an adult. Thus:

1. People featured in cigarette advertisements should be, and be clearly seen to be, adults of 25 or over.

2. Advertisements should not be designed, written or published in such a way as to make it likely that they will appeal more to those under 18 than to the public at large.

3. Characters and situations depicted should not be such as to inspire the emulation of the young, by suggesting that those who do not smoke at all, or who do not smoke a particular brand, are less grown up, less manly or less feminine than those who do or that they are lacking in daring or sophistication.

Appendix 4. Cigarette Promotion Code

The companies will take special care to ensure that promotional offers are directed only to adult smokers so as to reduce the possibility of their coming into the hands of young people, i.e. under 18 years of age. The companies will exercise this special care in ways that include the avoidance of anything that will appeal more particularly to such young people than to the public at large, the elimination as far as possible of such young people from mailing lists, and their restriction of hand-outs to adults, i.e. aged 18 or over who are smokers.

3. All promotional letters and leaflets containing offers should bear a prominent statement to the effect that the offer is restricted to smokers aged 18 or over.

6. All application forms for promotional offers will require the applicant to sign a statement that he or she is a smoker aged 18 or over.

Table 1 The exposure of tobacco sponsors' names and logos on BBC TV during tobacco sponsored sport broadcast in 1988 and 1989			
Sport	**Sponsor/date**	**Exposure of tobacco name/logo** secs/hour	**Thirty second advert equivalent**
Snooker	Embassy 1988	76	2
Snooker	Embassy 1989	176	6
Bowls	Embassy 1989	186	6
British Motor Racing	(Marlboro) 1988	290(1) 243(2)	10 8
Spanish Motor Racing	(Marlboro, Camel, Gitanes) 1989	167(3) 1177(4)	5 39

1. Static signs; 2. Logos on cars and participants; 3. Static signs; 4. Names and logos on cars and participants.

An extract from Beating the Ban: *an examination of tobacco sponsorship.*

No TV advertising of cigarettes has been allowed in Britain since 1965. Yet 64% of 9-15-year-olds claim to see cigarette advertising on TV.

Tobacco Consumption

When the real price of cigarettes increases, fewer adults smoke. We know that children are more affected by price increases than adults. Research has shown that fewer teenagers smoke and that those who do smoke reduce their consumption when there is a price increase.

"Five a day don't cost much" — "That's nearly £200 a year up in smoke"

Smoking. Who needs it?

Five a day don't cost much – *one of the press advertisements.*

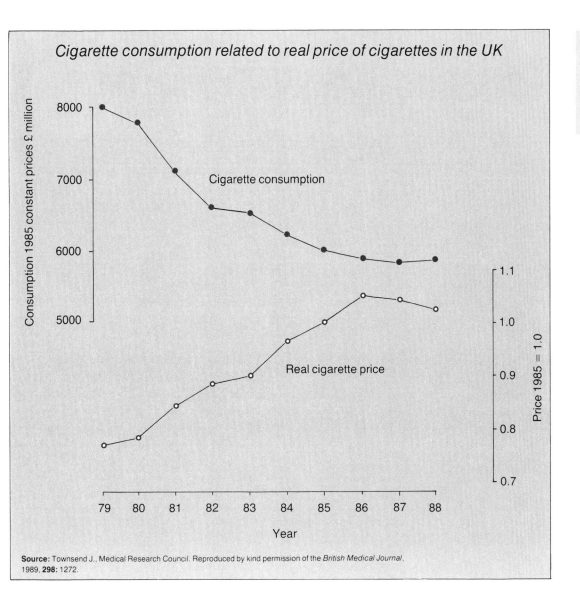

Cigarette consumption related to real price of cigarettes in the UK

Source: Townsend J., Medical Research Council. Reproduced by kind permission of the *British Medical Journal*, 1989, **298**: 1272.

Parents Against Tobacco

Parents Against Tobacco (PAT) is a campaign which aims to bring together parents, children, educators and the community at large in a combined exercise to protect young people from tobacco products. The main purpose of the campaign is that it must be made impossible for children under the age of 16 to buy cigarettes.

The campaign organisers have worked to create a 'tobacco blockade' between the tobacco industry and young people. Their objectives include:

- Exposing the way in which the law concerning the sale of tobacco products to children aged under 16 is ignored or inadequately enforced.
- Campaigning for a legal ban on all sales of tobacco products from vending machines, except in those premises reserved for the over-18s.
- Canvassing for the maximum fine (£400 at the time of writing) for selling cigarettes to under-16s to be increased to £1,000 with a £2,500 fine for a second offence and £10,000 for a third offence.
- Advocating legislation that makes it illegal to sell cigarettes in unbroken packets of ten or more.
- Encouraging the setting up of local PAT groups to carry out these objectives and to promote smoke-free zones for children, especially in schools.
- Organising the 'Pat on the Back' award scheme to encourage owners of small shops voluntarily to enforce the law on under-age sales (special PAT symbol available to participating retailers).
- Promoting 'PAT United' – a team of sports stars who individually visit schools

and make media appearances in support of the campaign.

Further information is available from:

Parents Against Tobacco
46 Arundel Street
Brighton BN2 5TH
Tel: 0273 601312

Note: As this publication goes to press, The Children and Young Persons (Protection from Tobacco) Bill is making progress through the Statute books. It proposes to increase the penalties for the sale of tobacco to persons under the age of 16 years; to make other amendments of section 7 of the Children and Young Persons Act 1933 and section 18 of the Children and Young Persons (Scotland) Act 1937; to prohibit the sale of unpackaged cigarettes; to require the publication of warning statements in retail premises and on vending machines; to make provision with respect to enforcement action by local authorities relating to offences connected with the sale of tobacco and to other matters; and for connected purposes.

SmokeBusters

SmokeBusters clubs promote lively, fun activities for youngsters aged 9–14. They offer one more component for a comprehensive strategy to promote a smoke-free environment for kids.

The aim is to help children resist taking up smoking by building on their own ideas and enthusiasm for not smoking. The name and concept originated from children.

Already more than 70,000 young people in the UK are members of SmokeBusters.

Typical club activities include competitions, pen-pal exchanges, discount schemes with local clothes and record shops, cafés and restaurants, cinemas and leisure centres.

For more information write to:

SmokeBusters UK
3-7 Clarence Chambers
39 Corporation Street
Birmingham B2 4LS
Tel: 021 633 4442

Useful Addresses

Action on Smoking and Health (ASH)
5–11 Mortimer Street
London W1N 7RN

British Heart Foundation
14 Fitzhardinge Street
London W1H 4DH

Cancer Research Campaign
Education and Child Studies Research
Group
Dept of Public Health and Epidemiology
Stopford Building
University of Manchester
Oxford Road
Manchester M13 9PT

Carbon Monoxide Monitors
Bedfont Technical Instruments Ltd
Bedfont House
Holywell Lane
Upchurch
Sittingbourne
Kent ME9 7HN

The Chest, Heart and Stroke Association
CHSA House
123–127 Whitecross Street
London EC1Y 8JJ

Cleanair
Campaign for a Smoke-free Environment
33 Stillness Road
London SE23 1NG

COMATAS
6th Floor
Clements House
Gresham Street
London EC2V 7DN

Coronary Prevention Group
60 Great Ormond Street
London WC1N 3NR

68

GASP
37 Stokes Croft
Bristol BS1 3PY

Health Education Authority
Hamilton House
Mabledon Place
London WC1H 9TX

Health Promotion Authority for Wales
Brunel House
2 Fitzalan Road
Cardiff CF2 1EB

Institute for the Study of Drug Dependence
(ISDD)
1–4 Hatton Place
Hatton Garden
London EC1N 8ND

Northern Ireland Health Promotion Unit
The Beeches
12 Hampton Manor Drive
Belfast BT7 3EN

Health Education Board for Scotland
Health Education Centre
Woodburn House
Canaan Lane
Edinburgh EH10 4SG

TACADE
1 Hulme Place
The Crescent
Salford M5 4QA

References

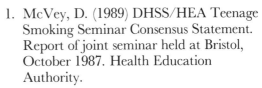

1. McVey, D. (1989) DHSS/HEA Teenage Smoking Seminar Consensus Statement. Report of joint seminar held at Bristol, October 1987. Health Education Authority.

2. Charlton, A. (1984) *The Brigantia Smoking Survey: A General Review. Public Education about Cancer.* UICC Technical Report Series 77, pp 92–102.

3. Nutbeam, D. (1984) *Smoking Prevalence among Schoolchildren: The Effects of Transfer to Secondary Education.* Paper presented at second conference on health education and youth. University of Southampton.

4. Flay, B.R. *et al.* in Worden, J.K. *et al.* 'Development of a smoking prevention mass media program using diagnostic and formative research', *Preventive Medicine* 17: 198, pp 521–58.

5. *CTN*, 17 July 1989.

6. HOC Hansard 147 – 8W 4.7.89. PQ to David Mellor MP.

7. HOC Hansard 1988/89 Session Vol. 146. Col. 268W 1.2.89.

8. Action on Smoking and Health. *The economic consensus of smoking in Northern Ireland: a cost benefit analysis of tobacco production and use in the province.* Belfast, ASH 1986.

9. Charlton, A. (1989) *Children and Passive Smoking.* Association for Non-Smokers' Rights, 2 St Stephen's Street, Edinburgh.

10. Bynner, J.M. (1969) *The Young Smoker . . . Smoking among Schoolboys.* London, HMSO.

11. Nelson, S.C. *et al.* (1985) 'The Avon Prevalence Study: a survey of cigarette smoking in secondary schoolchildren', *Health Education Journal* 44, p 12.

70

12. *Teenage Health and Lifestyles*, Health Education Authority. Forthcoming.

13. 'Evaluation of the carcinogenic risk of chemicals to humans: tobacco smoking' (Vol. 38 *IARC*, 1986, p 126) in *Health or Tobacco*. Toxic Substances Board, New Zealand Department of Health, 1989.

14. US Department of Health and Human Services (1989) *Reducing the Health Consequences of Smoking: 25 years of Progress. A Report of the Surgeon General.* Public Health Service, Centers for Disease Control. Center for Chronic Disease Prevention and Health Promotion, Office on Smoking and Health. 1989 DHHS Publication No. (CDC) 89-8411.

15. US Department of Health and Human Services (1988) *The Health Consequences of Smoking: Nicotine Addiction. A Report of the Surgeon General.*

16. Mangan, G.L. and Golding, J.F. (1984) *The Psychopharmacology of Smoking.* Cambridge University Press, London.

17. Wald, N., Doll, R. and Copeland, G. (1981) 'Trends in the tar, nicotine and carbon monoxide yields of UK cigarettes manufactured since 1934', *British Medical Journal* 282, pp 763-5.

18. Aston, H. and Stepney, R. (1982) *Smoking - Psychology and Pharmacology.* Tavistock Press, London.

19. Aronon, W.S. (1981) 'Effects of cigarette smoking and carbon monoxide in coronary heart disease', in Greenhalgh, R.M. (ed) *Smoking and Arterial Disease.* Pitman Medical, Bath.

20. Royal College of Physicians (1983) *Health or Smoking?* Pitman, London.

21. OPCS Mortality Statistics, HMSO, 1988.

22. Benetar, S.R. (1979) 'Smoking and chronic respiratory symptoms in 11–15 year old children', *South African Medical Journal* 56, pp 301-4.

23. Ward, L. (1984) *Facts about Smoking - A Trainer's Manual.* TACADE, Manchester.

24. S. Mackie. (ed) *ASH Tobacco 2 - Women and Smoking.* Scottish Committee on Action on Smoking and Health and Scottish Health Education Group.

25. Fourth Report of the Independent Scientific Committee on Smoking and Health. HMSO, 1988.

26. Jarvis, M. *et al.* (1987) 'Passive smoking in adolescents: one year stability of exposure in the home', *Lancet* 1, 1324-5.

27. Mitchell, L. (1990) *Growing Up in Smoke.* Pluto Press, London.

28. Bewley, B.R. and Bland, J.M. (1976) 'Smoking and respiratory symptoms in two groups of schoolchildren', *Preventive Medicine* 5, pp 63-9.

29. Safety in Science Laboratories, DES Safety Series, No. 21.

30. Safeguards in the School Laboratory, ASE.

31. *Smoking or Health.* Royal College of Physicians Report, London, 1977.

32. McNeill, A.D. *et al.* (1989) 'Nicotine intake in young smokers: longitudinal study of saliva cotinine concentrates', *American Journal of Public Health* 79: 2, pp 172-5.

33. Rigotti, N.A. (1989) 'Cigarette smoking and body weight', *New England Journal of Medicine* 320: 12, pp 931-3.

34. O'Connor, J. and Daly, M. (1985) *The Smoking Habit.* Gill and Macmillan, in association with the Health Education Bureau, Dublin.

35. Charlton, A. and Blair, V. (1989) 'Predicting the onset of smoking in boys and girls', *Social Science and Medicine* 29: 7, pp 813-18.

36. Charlton, A. (1987) 'Smoking related habits and references of 9 to 19 year olds in Northern England', *Hygie* VI: 146, pp 125-30.

37. Dickey, J.P. and Henderson, P. (1989) 'What young children say about stress and coping in school', *Health Education* 3.

38. Wills, T.A. (1986) 'Stress and coping in early adolescence: relationships to substance use in urban school samples', *Health Psychology* 5, pp 503–29.

39. *Teenage Girls and Smoking – An Expert Report of the ASH Women and Smoking Group.* Action on Smoking and Health, 1989.

40. Perry, C.L., Crockett, S.J. and Pirie, P. (1987) 'Influencing parental health behaviour: implications of community assessments', *Health Education*, October.

41. Aitken, P.P. (1980) 'Peer group pressures, parental controls and cigarette smoking among 10 to 14 year olds', *British Journal of Social and Clinical Psychology* 19, pp 141–6.

42. Murray, M., Kiryluk, S. and Swan, A.V. (1985) 'Relation between parents' and children's smoking behaviour and attitudes', *J. Epid. and Comm. Health* 39, pp 169–74.

43. Newman, I.M. and Ward, J.M. (1989) 'The influence of parental attitude and behaviour on early adolescent cigarette smoking', *Journal of School Health* 59: 4, pp 150–52.

44. Myers, K.A. (1989) An overview of school smoking policies in England and Wales. *Health Education Journal* 48: 3.

45. Charlton, A., Gillies, P. and Ledwith, F. (1985) 'Variations between school and regions in smoking prevalence among British schoolchildren: implications for health education', *Public Health* 99, pp 243–9.

46. Penny, G., Davies, D. and Robinson, J. (1988) 'Some correlates of the variability of adolescent smoking incidence between schools', *J. Inst. Health Educ.* 26: 1.

47. Dobbs, J. and Marsh, A. (1983) *Smoking among Secondary Schoolchildren.* OPCS Survey, London, HMSO.

48. Murray, M., Kiryluk, S. and Swan, A.V. (1984) 'School characteristics and adolescent smoking: results from the MRC/Derbyshire Smoking Study 1974–78 and from a follow-up in 1981', *J. Epid. Comm. Health* 38, pp 167–72.

49. Peers, I. (1987) *Smoking amongst Pupils and Staff in City Schools: Implications for Planning Health Education Programmes.* A baseline study prior to the implementation of Project Smoke Free Smoking Education Weeks. Health Education Authority, London.

50. Pentz, M.A. *et al.* (1989) 'The power of policy: the relationship of smoking policy to adolescent smoking', *American Journal of Public Health* 79: 7.

51. A survey of headteachers and health education co-ordinators. Research conducted by MORI. Health Education Authority. Forthcoming.

52. Aitkin, P.P. *et al.* (1988) 'Children and cigarette advertising' in *Pushing Smoke: Tobacco Advertising and Promotion (Smoke-free Europe: 8)*, World Health Organisation, Copenhagen.

53. Amos, A., Hillhouse, A. and Robertson, G. (1989) 'Tobacco advertising and children – the impact of the voluntary agreement', *Health Education Research* 4: 1, pp 51–7.

54. Jacobson, B. and Amos, A. (1985) *When Smoke Gets in Your Eyes!* British Medical Association.

55. Aitkin, P.P. and Eadie, D.R. (1990) 'Reinforcing effects of cigarette advertising on under-age smoking', *British Journal of Addiction* 85, pp 399–412.

56. Townsend, J. (1989) 'Cigarette smoking on increase', *British Medical Journal* 298: 1272.

57. Charlton, A. (1989) 'Anti-smoking and young people', *Modus* pp 175–7.

58. Department of Education and Science and the Welsh Office, *Science in the National Curriculum*, London, HMSO, 1989.

59. National Curriculum Council (1990), *Curriculum Guidance 5: Health Education.*

60. Williams, T., Wetton, N. and Moon, A. (1989) *A Way In: Five Key Areas of Health Education.* Health Education Authority.

61. Williams, T., Wetton, N. and Moon, A. (1989) *A Picture of Health.* Health Education Authority.

62. Goddard, E. (1989) *Smoking among Secondary School Children in England in 1988.* OPCS, HMSO.

63. Glynn, T.J. (1989) 'Essential elements of school-based smoking prevention programmes', *Journal of School Health* 59: 5, pp 181–8.

64. Brink, S.G. *et al.* (1988) 'Developing comprehensive smoking control programs in schools', *Journal of School Health* 58: 5, pp 17–180.

65. Kannas, L. (1988) 'Role and development of smoking prevention programmes in school', *Hygie* VII.

66. Schinke, S.J. *et al.* (1986) 'Skills methods to prevent smoking', *Health Education Quarterly* 13: 1, pp 23–7.

67. Worden, J.K. *et al.* (1987) 'An adult communication skills program to prevent adolescent smoking', *J. Drug Education* 17: 1.

68. Tortu, S. and Botvin, G. (1989) 'School-based smoking prevention: the teacher training process', *Preventive Medicine* 18, pp 257–66.

69. Silvestri, B. and Flay, B. (1989) 'Smoking education: comparison of practice and state-of-the-art', *Preventive Medicine* 18, pp 257–66.

70. Charlton, A., Melia, P. and Moyar, C. (1990) *A Manual on Tobacco and Young People for the Industrialized World.* IUCC, Geneva.

71. Reid, D. (1985) 'Prevention of smoking among schoolchildren: recommendation for policy development', *Health Education Journal* 44: 1.

72. Tones, B.K. (1986) 'Promoting the health of young people – the role of personal and social education', *Health Education Journal* 45: 1.

73. Tones, B.K. (1986) 'Health education and the ideology of health promotion: a review of alternative approaches', *Health Education Research* 1, pp 3–12.

74. Tones, B.K. (1987) 'Health education, PSE and the question of voluntarism', *J Inst. Educ.* 25: 2.

75. Andrews, R.L. and Hearne, J.T. (1984) 'The effects of an experimental primary grades curriculum project on student and parent smoking attitudes and behaviour', *Journal of School Health* 54: 1.

76. Charlton, A. (1984) 'Teachers' smoking habits', *Community Medicine* 6, p 273.

77. McGuffin, S.J., Hewitt, A.H. and Wood M.A. (1989) *A Survey of the Smoking Habit and Attitudes to Smoking of Teachers in Northern Ireland Schools.* Ulster Cancer Foundation/Action on Smoking and Health (Northern Ireland).

78. Charlton, A. (1985) 'So what is your school smoking policy?', *Education and Health* 3, pp 7–11.

79. King, R. (1973) *School Organisational and Pupil Involvement: A Study of Secondary School.* Routledge and Kegan Paul, London.

80. Newman, R. (1988) *Report on a Survey of Secondary School Teachers in South Glamorgan.* Health Authority/Heartbeat Wales.

81. Burghard, G. *et al.* (1979) 'The tobacco habit and respiratory symptoms among the adolescents of a French department', *Bulletin of the International Union against Tuberculosis* 54, pp 83–6.

82. Kannas, L. (1983) *The Right of Teachers to Smoke Devaluing Lessons*. PhD Thesis, University of Jyväsklä, Finland.

83. Newcombe, R.D. (1985) *School Policy Towards Smoking*. Report to the Health Education Council, London.

Orientation: School Checklist

- What is the local authority's position in relation to smoking:
    - among staff
    - among pupils
    - on school premises, grounds, etc.
    - on school trips and outings?
- What is the present school policy?

  Is it a formal written policy?

  When was it last reviewed?

  Has the issue of smoking been raised by:
    - parents
    - governors
    - teaching staff
    - non-teaching staff
    - pupils
    - PTA?
- What is the availability of cigarettes locally?
- Is smoking education in the curriculum?
    - when
    - how
    - by whom?
- Is smoking education systematic for all years?
- What materials are currently used?
- Is there liaison between schools about smoking education? Cross-phase?
- What help is available from the regional/local health authority/health education/health promotion centre?
- Is the local authority doing anything specifically to promote the smoke-free message?
- Is any other help available locally?

TOWARDS A SMOKE-FREE GENERATION: EVALUATION SHEET

Please let us have your comments on this manual. Fill in the sheet by putting a circle around the appropriate number for each statement. 1 = strongly disagree, 5 = strongly agree. Send it to the address below. Thank you.

Strongly   Strongly
disagree 1 2 3 4 5 agree

1. The manual provided all the information about smoking
   education that I needed.   1 2 3 4 5

2. If you disagreed with statement 1, what else should have been
   included?

3. It was easy to find the section(s) that I was most interested in.   1 2 3 4 5

4. Any other comments on layout, etc.

5. The following sections were useful to me:

Action summary	1	2	3	4	5
Introduction	1	2	3	4	5
Section 1 Impact of smoking on health	1	2	3	4	5
Section 2 Young people and smoking	1	2	3	4	5
Section 3 Influences on smoking and non-smoking	1	2	3	4	5
Section 4 Smoking and the curriculum	1	2	3	4	5
Section 5 Towards an effective school smoking policy	1	2	3	4	5
Section 6 School-based prevalence surveys	1	2	3	4	5
Section 7 Appendices	1	2	3	4	5

Strongly
disagree   1   2   3   4   5   Strongly
agree

6. There are suggestions for action in the manual. How practical do you feel these would be to carry out? Please give reasons for your answer.

7. Other comments relating to the usefulness of the manual.

8. Any other general comments about the manual.

9. Type of school   Primary

   (please circle)   Middle

                        Secondary

                        Other (please specify)

10. Are you involved with:

    smoking education ☐
    health education   ☐
    science   ☐

Thank you for your help. Please return to: Young People's Setting, Health Education Authority, Hamilton House, Mabledon Place, London WC1H 9TX.